THE REAL SHERLOCK HOLMES
Arthur Conan Doyle

BORN: May 22, 1859
DIED: July 7, 1930

Few writers have created such an illusion of reality
as did Arthur Conan Doyle in Sherlock Holmes
and his friend Dr. Watson. So convincing is the
tall, hawk-faced sleuth with his deer-hunter's cap
and briar pipe, scholars still argue that he must
have been a real person. Whatever that controversy,
Arthur Conan Doyle was indeed a very real and
very active man—athlete, doctor, politician, war
correspondent, champion of lost causes. He was involved in nearly every major event that occurred in
his long life (1859–1930), and his own adventures,
his interest in scientific detection, plus a very fer-
tile imagination, all found their way into his stories
about Sherlock Holmes.

BOOKS BY MARY HOEHLING

THADDEUS LOWE
  America's One-Man Air Corps

GIRL SOLDIER AND SPY
  Sarah Emma Edmundson

YANKEE IN THE WHITE HOUSE
  John Quincy Adams

THE REAL SHERLOCK HOLMES
  Arthur Conan Doyle

THE REAL
SHERLOCK
HOLMES

Arthur Conan Doyle

by

Mary Hoehling

Julian Messner
New York

Published by Julian Messner
Division of Pocket Books, Inc.
8 West 40 Street, New York 10018

© Copyright 1965 by Mary Hoehling

Second Printing, 1966

Printed in the United States of America
Library of Congress Catalog Card No. 65-12952

Acknowledgments

I wish to express my gratitude to the children of Sir Arthur Conan Doyle for the help and encouragement they have given me during the preparation of this story of their father's life:

To Mary Conan Doyle, who diligently searched her memory for personal recollections.

To Adrian Conan Doyle, whose collection of his father's letters and manuscripts at Geneva, Switzerland, is a boon to the biographer, as are his own books and reminiscences.

And to Air Commandant Dame Jean Conan Doyle, D.B.E., A.D.C.

Special thanks, too, to Leslie Reade, London lawyer and writer, who worked briefly with Sir Arthur on the Oscar Slater case, for his personal recollections and his articles in the *London Evening News*.

And to my husband, A. A. Hoehling, whose curiosity sparked this book.

Contents

THE REAL SHERLOCK HOLMES
Arthur Conan Doyle

I have wrought my simple plan
If I give one hour of joy
To the boy who's half a man,
Or the man who's half a boy.

ARTHUR CONAN DOYLE

1. "Tarts Down and Strictly Business"

Young Arthur Conan Doyle trudged homeward through the narrow streets of Edinburgh, Scotland. The afternoon had passed all too swiftly as he sat in a hidden corner of the free library reading his favorite author. Mayne Reid's adventure tales could transport an imaginative nine-year-old right out of grimy Edinburgh to the trackless wilderness of North America. Today Arthur had escaped capture by the Indians by lying submerged in a stream while breathing through a hollow reed.

This evening, a fine April mist mingled with the smoke that always shrouded the industrial city. The lamplighter had not yet passed when Arthur stepped into the street. In the waning light, the swirls of fog took threatening forms. At each corner lurked a silent savage; a wild beast crouched behind each hitching post. Arthur began to whistle as he hurried along swinging his book bag like a weapon.

As he approached Sciennes Hill Place where he lived, the sound of shouting hurried his footsteps. His eyes watered as he strained to see through the acrid smog. Suddenly a tall figure, one lanky arm waving a long green sack, cavorted into sight.

"Into the gutter, old woman," a voice rasped. "Leave the pavement to yer betters."

That's no wraith, thought Arthur, angrily. It's that bully Jed Brown that runs errands for the cobbler. Who's he plaguing now?

A bent shadow cowered against the wall of a house. Arthur recognized the pathetic little body as an ancient ragpicker he often saw scavenging in the back alleys. Carefully setting his book bag on a doorstep, he strode across the street, demanding loudly, "Why don't you pick on someone your own size?"

The bootmaker's errand boy swung around to see who was challenging him. Nine-year-old Arthur was heavily built but far shorter and less developed than fourteen-year-old Jed.

"Well, look who's askin' for trouble!" Jed cried scornfully. "Go back to yer books, featherhead, and leave man's work to men."

Righteous anger welled up in Arthur. "What kind of man would pick on a poor defenseless creature like that?" he asked. But as he pointed to where the old woman had stood, he realized she had taken advantage of the diversion to slip away.

In the same moment, Jed Brown also saw that his quarry had escaped. With a shout of fury he turned on Arthur. There was a flash of green as he swung his bag, heavy with workmen's boots not yet delivered. Arthur saw a jagged row of yellow teeth in the ugly grimacing face, then—nothing.

It was past seven when Arthur stumbled into the scrubbed kitchen of his home at 3 Sciennes Hill Place. His head ached and he felt dizzy. He sank quietly into a kitchen chair beside his eldest sister Annette, who never lifted her eyes from the book she was reading. Seven-year-old Lottie was absorbed in amusing the toddler Connie. Through the doorway, he could see his father peering nearsightedly at an easel propped up on the dining room table.

His mother was cleaning the grate, the vigorous thump-

thump of her hearth brush enlivening the scene. Arthur could never recall a time when she was idle.

"I've kept your stew warm," Mrs. Doyle said without turning, "though you're late enough, heaven knows, that I should send you off to bed without your supper!"

When Arthur did not reply, nor make a move to get his plate, she straightened and looked around. Her gasp of surprise focused all eyes on him, while she stood motionless, the hearth brush still poised for action. Her other hand, encased in a sooty glove, grasped a piece of coal.

"You've been fighting again!" she announced.

Arthur looked down sadly at his torn muddy coat, the sleeves hardly covering his scrawny hands and wrists. It was old and much-mended already, but would have to be cleaned and mended once more.

"I'm sorry, Ma'am," Arthur said sincerely.

But Mary Doyle was looking at the swelling on her son's forehead. "Annette, fetch some water from the well," she commanded. "Now sit here and eat your supper—if you can," she told Arthur, "—and tell us just how you got such a lump!"

While Annette applied rags soaked in the cold well water, Arthur described his encounter with Jed Brown.

"You have acted in the proud tradition of your ancestors," Mrs. Doyle admitted when she understood the circumstances. She never ceased to remind them all that they were descended on both sides from ducal houses.

"You must ever be fearless to the strong, humble to the weak, chivalrous toward all women of high and low degree." Mary Doyle concluded her little speech with a dramatic wave of the stew ladle.

Supper and Annette's nursing, plus the knowledge that he had acted in true knightly tradition, combined to make Arthur's head feel much better. "And the books didn't even get soiled," he announced, drawing them from the bag. "I got *Rob Roy* by Sir Walter Scott and *Le Voyage au Centre de la Terre* by Jules Verne."

"Sir Walter, too, is distantly related," Mrs. Doyle reminded her family for the hundredth time.

"Very distantly." Charles Doyle broke his customary silence. He looked on his wife's intense family pride with wry humor. "Mary blows the trumpet enough," he often observed.

Mary Foley Doyle had something to "blow" about. Her mother, Catherine Pack, traced her ancestry to the ancient ducal house of Percy-Louvain and claimed alliance by marriage with the royal Plantagenets. Charles Doyle, though a lowly clerk in His Majesty's Office of Works at Edinburgh, came from a family of Irish country squires, the D'Oyleys of Stoke Doyley; his mother had been a Conan, a family rooted in the ducal house of Brittany.

Mary Doyle had studied heraldry in France where she had been educated. She spoke French as fluently as English, and through her, Arthur had learned his love of history and reading. Busy as she was, she always seemed to have a book in her hand. She could read while knitting, even when feeding her babies. The family joked that once when she had become so absorbed in her book, she deposited a spoonful of rusk and milk in Connie's ear when the child turned her head.

With her gentle manner and intellectual turn of mind, Mrs. Doyle was as out of place in their tough neighborhood as a rose in a cabbage patch. The same could be said of Mr. Doyle, though this was the best he could afford on his government salary. He had a detached aloofness that led his neighbors to believe him a snob, and his constant "daubing" with paints confirmed their opinion that Charles Doyle was really "quite odd!"

Charles was the only Doyle who had not made a name for himself. Arthur's grandfather John had been famous in the London art world, and was known as "HB" to art lovers, Uncle Henry Doyle, CB, managed the National Gallery at Dublin, while Uncle Richard was the "Dicky" Doyle of *Punch*. His whimsical drawings on the cover of that popular magazine had made him famous. He had also illustrated Charles Dickens' *Christmas Stories* and William Makepeace Thackeray's *The Newcomes*. Uncle James was a writer who shared Mary Doyle's interest in heraldry. He emblazoned the family crests on large sheets of cardboard which she used to illustrate her lectures. Arthur learned them all by heart with his multiplication tables.

Friends of Arthur's famous uncles often dropped in at Sciennes Hill Place, and when their carriages rumbled into the street, it delighted him to watch the heads appear at every window down the block. Thackeray had been among those visitors.

One of Arthur's earliest memories was of sitting on the knee of the portly white-bearded author, whose kindly eyes twinkled at him through steel-rimmed spectacles, as he held Thackeray's great gold watch. The experience inspired Arthur's first literary effort—a story written in bold print on lined foolscap, two words to a line. It was all about swords and guns and Bengal tigers, and he discovered that it was easier to get his hero into trouble than to get him out.

Arthur often wondered why his father had not succeeded like his brothers. He did not even try to sell his paintings but gave them away to friends, though his family certainly could have used the money. Only his pen and ink illustrations brought in any revenue.

"People don't appreciate Papa's work," Annette told Arthur once. Neither child would admit that Father's paintings seemed strange, even eerie, to them too.

"Now don't go into the family history tonight, Mary," Charles Doyle begged. "Arthur's had a nasty bump and should get some rest."

"Well, I had hoped he could read aloud from the new Verne book tonight while I sew," Mrs. Doyle replied reluctantly. "Annette can read, of course, but his French pronunciation does need improvement."

When all the children had gone to bed, the Doyles discussed their plans for Arthur's future. "It will be only a few more weeks till the boy goes to the Jesuits at Hodder," Mr. Doyle reminded his wife.

"And just in time, I'd say. I'll certainly miss him here at home. He'd as soon rock his little sister to sleep as fight the neighborhood bullies. But this is no place to bring up a young gentleman. I can watch the girls, but a boy . . ." Mary Doyle threw up her hands. "Thank goodness for your Uncle Michael Conan!"

Arthur's Granduncle Michael Conan was his godfather too. An art critic and editor of the magazine *Art Journal*, he made his home on the Avenue de Wagram in Paris. Though he had never seen his godson, he kept in constant touch with his progress. He had always urged a Jesuit education.

"In mere secular education," he counseled, "the Jesuits are of the highest order of mind, unmatched."

The whole family went with Arthur to the station that September to see him off to boarding school. They stood in a woebegone group on the train platform, his mother and sisters weeping unashamedly. As the ten-year-old boy climbed aboard the Liverpool express, he stanchly held back his tears, but as the train crossed the Scottish border into northern England his tears flowed unchecked. Only when they puffed to a halt at the Preston station, just north of Liverpool, and Arthur saw a group of boys and a black-robed priest waiting near a big farm wagon, did he resume his stolid mask.

"None of the masters could be so bad as that one-eyed, pock-marked rascal I've endured for two years," he consoled himself for the hundredth time as he struggled down the train steps with his carpetbag.

The fathers at Hodder were strict, but the principal, Father Cassidy, insisted that they "be gentle with the little rascals."

Arthur became accustomed to being awakened at six o'clock in the morning by a policeman's rattle. He shivered and grew tough in the unheated dormitory and study room when the winter winds off the Irish Sea whistled across the flat Lancashire countryside.

The school year was broken only by the summer or a long holiday. The gray days flowed by in a weary grind of singsong lessons in Latin, mathematics, grammar. Even history, so exciting as his mother told it, became a monotony of dates.

He never neglected his weekly letter home, and wrote with enthusiasm about cricket and football, ice-skating and hockey. He was learning to box properly, ". . . and I believe I could beat up any of those bullies now!" he wrote proudly.

Yet always inside him was a dull ache of homesickness, and a sadness at never having known his new baby brother Frank, who died shortly after birth.

At twelve, Arthur graduated from Hodder to the Jesuit college of Stonyhurst, an old castle only a mile away. The vaulted rooms were as cold as they were grand. The boys were required to take an overwhelming number of classes— elements, figures, rudiments, grammar, syntax, poetry and rhetoric, Euclid, algebra, the classics. All the subjects were taught in a manner so medieval that Arthur thought no one could learn anything but hatred for them.

The boys were fortified for the day's work by a meager predawn breakfast of dry bread and hot milk liberally cut with water. By noon they were as hungry as wolves. Meat or fish was served at noonday dinner, but tea was a tasteless drink the boys called "beer." Only at supper were they allowed butter with their bread and sometimes, as a treat, potatoes. Twice a week they were given pudding.

The suspicious attitude of the fathers, who watched the boys day and night, infuriated Arthur. Before he had been at Stonyhurst a month, he was introduced to the Tolley, an instrument of discipline brought by the Jesuits from Holland. Caught whispering at Mass once too often, he was taken to a small room back of the headmaster's study. The black-robed priest picked up from a table a piece of India rubber about the size and shape of a thick boot sole.

"Hold out your left hand," he commanded.

The first blow on Arthur's palm made an angry red welt. The unexpected intensity of the pain caused him to grunt.

"The minimum punishment is nine blows on one hand," the priest told him.

Arthur bit his lip so not another sound could escape, but inside he raged at the unjust severity of the punishment. Every instinct cried out to fight back, as he had fought the ruffians on the streets of Edinburgh.

"Older boys and repeaters will receive nine blows on *each* hand," warned the priest when he had finished, but Arthur hardly heard him as he fumbled with the doorknob. If he did not get out fast, he was afraid he would hit the holy father with his good right hand.

From that time on, Arthur seemed to take pleasure in outrageous behavior, as if to prove he could not be cowed by violence. The fathers never guessed that an appeal to his better nature would have found a ready answer. He became so lazy in his studies that he was often made to leave his desk and kneel in the middle of the classroom holding his books in his arms. He took his punishment quietly, a strange fixed smile hiding his growing hatred for the stern discipline and rigid teachings.

Kneeling on the cold floor, he tried to forget his aching muscles by making up verses about the masters and boys. The results made him famous among his classmates.

The boys discovered, too, that he could spin a blood-chilling yarn or an adventure story that transported them away from the frigid gray halls of Stonyhurst. On a rainy holiday, he sat on a desk while they squatted in a circle around him listening to his tales of mystery and suspense.

Arthur was too wily to talk himself hoarse for nothing. His stomach was always empty, and his allowance for pastries too small.

"Remember, lads, it's tarts down and strictly business," he reminded them, and they nodded expectantly.

The lowering sky, the rain or hail pounding against the window panes, the wind howling round the ancient towers, lent a fitting atmosphere to the ghostly figments of young Arthur's imagination.

"With his left hand in her glossy locks, he was waving the bloodstained knife above her head, when . . ." he whispered, then paused dramatically.

One glance at his rapt audience satisfied him that his supply of goodies was assured for weeks to come.

2. "Do You Want to Be a Doctor?"

Sports, especially cricket, were Arthur's favorite pastime.

"When I reside at Edinburgh," he wrote his mother in February, 1873, "I would like to enter some cricket club there. It is a jolly game, and does more to make a fellow strong and healthy than all the doctors in the world. I think I could take a place in the eleven of any club in Edinburgh."

He was certainly big enough. At fourteen, he was growing so fast that the priests feared he would burst his clothes. Below his frayed cuffs, his big bony hands and skinny wrists were always red with cold. His knickerbockers barely covered his knees.

"But my cricket clothes fit very well," Arthur told the Ma'am, his affectionate term for his mother. "Thank you for the noble necktie and the lime cream for my hair. I look quite the dandy."

He mentioned his appearance only to reassure her. He knew she could not afford to buy him new clothes. Even with help from Uncle Michael Conan, his family had to stretch each penny in order to provide him with an education.

That spring another baby was born, a healthy boy with

21

a firm hold on life. During the long holiday, Arthur took over the care and feeding of his little brother Innes, playing with him as enthusiastically as a young father.

On his return to Stonyhurst, Arthur tackled his studies with renewed vigor.

"Translating Homer and Virgil is laborious," he wrote Uncle Michael Conan, "and makes the study of the classics a horror. I learn only enough to want to know more, yet we are not even given an idea what the age was like in which these events took place! I should think an intelligent person could learn more from a good translation."

Wise old Uncle Conan's reply was a small book with gilt edges, Lord Macaulay's *Lays of Ancient Rome*. The book became Arthur's constant companion. He hid it under his pillow where he could draw it out in the night when the sentinel priest was at the other end of the dormitory or had dozed off in a rare moment of human weakness.

By the dim light of the candles, Arthur thrilled to the poet's ringing lines. Soon he had memorized the "Lay of Horatius." He could lie with eyes closed, repeating it, while thrilling pictures danced before his imagination.

> Then up spake brave Horatius,
>   The Captain of the Gate. . . .
> Hew down the bridge, Sir Consul,
>   With all the speed ye may;
> I, with two more to help me,
>   Will hold the foe in play . . .

That term, all the students were required not only to read but also to write poetry. The exercise was pure torture to most of the boys, but Arthur delighted in the rhymes and cadence. With apparent ease, he turned out quantities of verse, mailing it to Uncle Conan.

"There can be no doubt of his faculty for that accomplishment," Michael Conan wrote Mrs. Doyle.

The Jesuit fathers apparently agreed with Arthur's godparent. In a class competition he won first place for a long epic about the crossing of the Red Sea.

> Like pallid daisies in a grassy wood,
> So round the sward the tents of Israel stood . . .

Suspense built up as Pharaoh's army hemmed in the fleeing Israelites on the shores of the Red Sea:

> There was no time for thought and none for fear,
> For Egypt's horse already pressed their rear . . .

Arthur found it hard to believe that the fathers had actually awarded him something besides punishment.

That Christmas of 1874, he made his first trip to London to visit his father's sister Annette, who kept house for Uncle Dick.

"It is 14° below freezing," he replied excitedly to his aunt's invitation, "but no ice-locked roads will keep me from getting to the nearest railway station."

Arthur frowned thoughtfully. How would she know him in the crowded railway station? He dipped his pen in the inkwell and added: "I believe I am 5 feet 9 inches high, pretty stout, clad in dark garments and, above all, with a flaring red muffler round my neck."

There were three accidents on the Lancashire railways which made the train hours late getting into London. To add to the passengers' discomfort, the cars were unheated. Fortunately, some of them carried rugs which they shared willingly with Arthur. When they finally arrived in gloomy Euston Station, his red muffler served as a beacon for Aunt Annette. She spotted her fifteen-year-old nephew the moment he descended from the train, and whisked him away to his Uncle Dick's studio in Finborough Road.

Arthur remained in London three magic weeks. Balding and affable Uncle Dick was free with both pocket money and time. He bought him a proper topcoat, then showed him the sights, from the majestic cathedral of St. Paul's to the zoo. Bearded, dignified Uncle James took him to see the popular actor Henry Irving in *Hamlet*.

More exciting was the visit to the Haymarket Theater to see *Our American Cousin,* which had been playing at Ford's Theater in Washington when Abraham Lincoln was shot. Arthur was far more interested in the tragedy than in the play itself.

Violence and mystery fascinated him. He could imagine all sorts of weird and evil doings in the foggy gaslit streets of London, as he watched the mud-splattered cabs moving soundlessly along the wet pavements. On such an evening he found his way to Madame Tussaud's Wax-works in Baker Street.

"I was delighted," he wrote his mother, "with the room of horrors, and the images of the murderers!"

Arthur's first and last visits while in London were to Westminster Abbey. The first time he went, he spent hours wandering through the crypt examining the effigies of kings and clergy buried there, and reading all the plaques that marked the graves of statesmen, artists and writers. But on his last day in London, he hurried straight to the grave of Macaulay and stood there quietly, hat in hand.

When he returned to Stonyhurst, Arthur studied like a demon.

"I want to qualify to take the London matric this spring," he told Jim Ryan, his dormitory neighbor.

The matriculation examinations at London University each spring must be passed by all boys wishing to enter a

British university. The requirements were frightening—
English language and history, French, Latin and Greek
grammar, a book of Homer, philosophy, chemistry, algebra,
arithmetic, Euclid. If you did not measure up in every subject, you were disqualified in all.

"With your memory for details, you should have no trouble," Jim assured his friend.

"Still I'm worried over the exams," Arthur admitted. "My
mother is determined that I go on to the university. So I
must qualify or spend another year here. I believe if I get
up to London, I'll pass all right. T'is the trial here that's my
bugbear, knowing the fathers have it in for me."

His professors were less surprised than Arthur when he
not only qualified for the matric, but also made honors.

"But sixteen is young for the university," Father Pur-
brick, the Rector, told Arthur. "How would you like a year
at our school in Feldkirch, Austria? A year abroad would
give you academic finish and wouldn't hurt your German."

Delighted at the thought of getting away from Stonyhurst,
Arthur readily agreed.

It was a sunny day early in September, 1875, when he
arrived in Feldkirch, wearing a new tweed suit and a peaked
cap. His box perched jauntily on his shoulder as he marched
along a mountain path, stopping every now and then to
admire the view. The tile-roofed cottages snuggled in the
shadow of the snow-peaked Alps. Six thousand feet above the
town hung the Pass of Arlberg, ancient highway into Switzerland. Guarding the pass stood a medieval fortress that was
now the Jesuit school. He took deep breaths of the clear
mountain air; it was a welcome change after the eternal
damp of Lancashire.

But I'll bet the atmosphere in there is just as cold and
grim as at Stonyhurst, he thought dourly as he approached
the forbidding pile of stone.

Arthur's first pleasant surprise was the cheery wood fires that were burning at either end of the dormitory. They hardly took the chill from the long high-vaulted gallery, but their very presence was heartwarming. The food at supper was plentiful and good. With it was served a delicious light beer instead of the horrible "swipes" the boys had endured at Stonyhurst.

"Just wait till you take a wrong step, m'boy," he told himself as he rolled into bed. "Then we'll see how kindly the place is after all."

Tired from his long trip and the excitement of arrival, he was dozing off when loud snoring echoed through the room, bringing him upright in bed. Cots on either side of the room stretched away into the darkness, their occupants quiet and evidently untroubled. Arthur rolled over beneath the covers. The sound roared over the sleeping figures again.

"I'll put a stop to that," Arthur muttered.

On each side of the narrow bed were crossed wooden pieces which had something to do with holding up the cots. As he started to get out of bed to silence the snorer, the wooden pieces moved beneath his hand; only a little effort was necessary to get one of them loose.

Quietly Arthur moved along the rows of bed until he located the snorer. Poking the lad vigorously, he hissed in very bad German, "You're making too much noise."

The reaction was like a clap of thunder that wakened the whole dormitory. Arthur turned to find the black-robed priest who monitored the room glaring down at him in the half-light of a candle.

But the only punishment was a lecture from the Rector on his "free and easy English ways."

"Have you ever played in a band?" the Rector asked as Arthur turned to leave. "The lad who played the bombardon did not return this fall. You look husky enough for it."

He admitted that he did not play any musical instrument,

but he thought it might be fun. He told the Rector he would do his best.

Arthur was turned over to the bandmaster who presented him with the largest brass horn he had ever seen. The monster wound twice around his broad shoulders and emitted a deep "whoom."

"Blowing it," he wrote his family, "is splendid work for the chest."

He practiced every free moment until both masters and boys began to entertain thoughts of murder. Once some boys stuffed the huge horn with bedding; another time they put limburger cheese in the mouthpiece. But Arthur tooted on.

Within a week he was playing in public with the band. His contribution was an accompanying "boomp-boomp" and an occasional run, "like a hippopotamus doing a step-dance."

Tobogganing and football took the place of cricket that winter. There were long hikes across the mountains during which Arthur expounded at length to the German boys on the glories of England and the unparalleled exploits of her navy.

He founded the *Feldkirch Newspaper,* with the motto: "Fear not and put it in print." Several issues were printed before the fathers quashed it for living up to its motto too well. Arthur had printed for the first time some of his own poems—"The Infuriated Cabman" and "Figaro's Farewell" —which Uncle Conan declared showed "original freshness and imaginative refinement."

Arthur returned to Edinburgh in June, 1876, traveling by way of Paris, where he met for the first time his loyal Great-uncle Conan. He liked the volcanic old French-Irishman immediately, sensing a kinship of mind and spirit. The two spent many hours together in the little walled garden behind the house on the Avenue de Wagram, while birdlike Aunt Susan fluttered lovingly nearby. She tended her husband's every need, for age and weight had weakened his legs. But Michael Conan's mind was sharp and penetrating, with a quality of insight not always found in more active men.

"You'd do well to think of a literary career," he often repeated, as he had in his letters.

However, Arthur maintained that his efforts along literary lines were nothing but the amusement of a schoolboy.

"Mother would like me to study medicine at Edinburgh University," he told his uncle. "It's one of the finest medical schools in the world."

Uncle Conan's eyes were narrowed against the setting sun. His lips pursed between his luxuriant white mustache and neat pointed beard.

"A medical career will put a strain on your family," the old man warned. "Four years, maybe five . . ."

"I believe I can win a scholarship or bursary. I'm pretty sure of myself in chemistry."

Uncle Conan reached out a gnarled hand to finger the book on conic sections that Arthur had laid aside while they spoke. Another book lay open beneath it. Michael Conan knew without looking that it was a collection of stories by Edgar Allen Poe.

"Do you want to be a doctor, Arthur?" he asked softly.

Arthur did not answer at once. Light from the setting sun filtered through the chestnut tree whose branches hung over the garden wall. A pungent odor from Aunt Susan's kitchen hung in the soft air. It had been a wonderful year, especially this past month in Paris. In many ways he would like to stay here with Uncle Conan, but his heart longed for bleak Edinburgh. In his mind's eye he saw his family gathered in the kitchen. There was a new sister, Ida, whom he had never seen.

"Yes," he answered finally. "I suppose it will be a good thing to study medicine."

3. Years of Discontent

Life at Edinburgh University was gay and carefree after six years with the Jesuits. Students chose their courses, attended lectures at will. Their social life was their own concern.

Arthur welcomed the freedom. At seventeen, he was a strong, well-developed athlete with a zest for life.

"His size suggests a steady income in coal heaving or furniture moving," Mr. Doyle commented, eyeing his son's bulky six feet that seemed to overcrowd the low-ceilinged kitchen.

To keep down expenses, the Doyles now shared an old townhouse with another family. The big bright kitchen of Sciennes Hill Place had been exchanged for a dingy basement room.

"With that chest he should take up professional wrestling," joked Lottie. "He always did like to fight!"

"Well, he'll do neither," asserted Mrs. Doyle. "With his mind and background, t'would be sinful if he did not take his degree!"

"Now, Ma'am, a degree would mean five more years!" Arthur protested. "A license to practice is enough for now. I can do that in three, and start earning some money."

His father's health was failing, and he might be forced to retire soon from the Office of Public Works. The pension of a government clerk would barely sustain so large a family. Besides Innes and the baby, Lottie and Connie were still in school. Only Annette contributed to the Doyles' slender income. She had taken a post as governess with a wealthy family in Portugal.

"Why so far away?" asked Arthur.

"An English governess is considered very chic on the continent as well in America," his mother told him. "Your sisters can command twice the salary by going abroad to work!"

A feeling of responsibility to his family depressed Arthur's usually exuberant nature. So did the prospect of five more years of grind at botany, chemistry, anatomy, physiology. It seemed to him that many courses required for a medical degree had little bearing on the science of healing.

In August he entered the scholarship competition and a week later was informed that he had won the Grierson bursary of forty pounds for two years. When he went to the university office to claim his prize, the official was puzzled.

"There must be some mistake," he said. "This bursary is offered only to arts students."

"Well surely I will get a comparable purse available for medicals?" protested Arthur.

"Oh I am sorry, young man," the official replied. "All the medical bursaries have been claimed!"

In the end Arthur received a pitifully inadequate seven pounds from some obscure fund for needy medical students.

The work was difficult and often dull, but he discovered that his professors offered diversion.

"We manage to know them pretty well without any personal contact," he noted in the journal he had begun.

In his second year, Arthur studied and practiced at the

Edinburgh Infirmary under Dr. Joseph Bell, a renowned
surgeon.

> The most notable of the characters whom I met [he
> wrote], was one Joseph Bell, surgeon at the Edinburgh
> Infirmary. He was thin, wiry, dark, with a high-nosed, acute
> face, penetrating grey eyes, angular shoulders, and a jerky
> way of walking. His voice was high and discordant. He was
> a very skillful surgeon, but his strong point was diagnosis,
> not only of disease, but of occupation and character.

Students swarmed after Dr. Bell as he made his way
through the wards, and strained to hear his comments as he
poked and tapped his patients. His keen gray eyes singled
out Arthur's bulky frame the very first day.

"You must be my outpatient clerk," he rasped, pointing
a bony finger at Arthur. "Ready the patients for examination. Take a few notes on their background. You'll receive
a small fee for the service."

Dr. Bell interviewed his clinic patients on a raised platform in the lecture hall. Surrounded by his orderlies and
students, he looked like an alert, scrawny bird. Arthur's first
case was a man with grotesquely swollen limbs.

"Well, my man, you've served in the Army I see," Bell
snapped. It was a statement, not a question. Yet the doctor
had not looked at his clerk's notes.

"Aye, sir," was the reply.

"Not long discharged?"

"No, sir."

"A Highland regiment?"

"Aye, sir."

"A noncommissioned officer?"

"Aye, sir."

"Stationed at Barbados?"

"Aye, sir."

Dr. Bell glanced at his amazed audience. Then he jumped up and paced the platform as he explained how he had deduced so many facts.

"You see, gentlemen, the man is a respectful man, yet he did not remove his hat. In the army they do not. But he has not been long discharged or he would have learned civilian ways. His speech tells us he is a Scot. His air of authority marks him as an officer, but other factors point to the noncommissioned rather than the regular officer—a sergeant or corporal, I should think. As to Barbados—that was simple, gentlemen. He complains of elephantiasis, a disease found in the West Indies, never in Britain!"

Working so closely with Dr. Bell, Arthur came to know him better than his other professors. Sometimes they walked home together in the cold winter twilight, and Arthur questioned him about his astonishing deductions.

"How did you happen to pick me for your clerk?" he wondered.

"Observation, my boy, is the basis of an intelligent diagnosis, and a diagnosis is, after all, a medical deduction based on physical symptoms. One observes with the senses—the eyes, the ears, the fingertips, yes, even the nose. Unfortunately most people never learn to use their senses properly.

"Now in your case—my eyes were assaulted by your bigness. Forgive me, but to say you stand out in a crowd is elementary, what? For the rest—I saw frayed cuffs and mended trousers, an honest, intelligent face. The textbook under your arm was so worn it must have been at least third-hand. Add a cold pipe sticking out of the pocket of that ancient tweed jacket . . ." Dr. Bell shrugged. "In an instant the facts enter the brain and a message comes back—'Here is an earnest student who can use some extra money.'"

As they walked, Arthur had been chewing on his pipe. He

had started smoking in Austria, but these days he could seldom afford tobacco.

"But how could you know my pipe was cold?"

"Most students tap out their pipes just before entering the hospital. The warm embers have a distinct odor. And what sort of man chews a cold pipe? An intense man who is too preoccupied or too short of pocket money to stoke it."

During the summer of 1878, after his second year of medical school, poverty forced Arthur to seek a position as a doctor's assistant. His first employer, Dr. James Richardson, practiced in the poorest sections of Sheffield, in England's industrial midlands. Over the whole area hung a pall of coal smoke heavier than that over Edinburgh. Everyone had a pallid wasted look, as well as a racking cough.

Arthur's chief job was to compound the medicines prescribed by Dr. Richardson and dispense them to the patients. They looked so ragged and wasted that, too often, the kindhearted medical student could not bring himself to take their shillings and pence.

"You'll ruin me!" roared Dr. Richardson, and discharged him after only three weeks.

Since he was nearer London than Edinburgh, Arthur decided to advertise for a position there, and incidentally visit his Doyle uncles and dear Aunt Annette, now living in Clifton Gardens, Maida Vale. Aunt Annette mothered him just as she had when he was a boy, filling him with her superbly cooked puddings and roasts. Uncle Dick and Uncle James were kind as ever, but the warmth and magic were gone from the relationship. Arthur found the older men stuffy and conventional, while they obviously considered him too Bohemian for their taste.

"Besides, I feel an awful hypocrite with them," Arthur confided to his old friend, Jim Ryan, as they walked in Kensington Gardens one day. "They are devout Catholics, as you know, and speak of placing me with a good Catholic doctor. Yet I hesitate to tell them I cannot accept so narrow a theology!"

"Have you become the complete scientist then?"

"I am not an agnostic, though many of my fellow students do go so far as to deny the existence of God altogether," Arthur mused. "I believe the Nature of God is beyond the understanding of mere man, and I've made up my mind never to accept that which cannot be proved."

Arthur almost joined the Army so desperate was he to find employment. Under Queen Victoria and her canny Prime Minister, Disraeli, Britain's colonial power had reached deep into Africa and India. The armies that conquered and held those faraway lands were always in need of young men. Recruiting officers haunted Trafalgar Square to lure the unwary with tales of glamour.

"T'would break your mother's heart," Jim warned when he saw his friend was tempted.

Arthur had decided to try for a surgeon's post in the Navy, even discussed the move with his uncles, when a Dr. Elliot of Shropshire replied to his ad. Arthur spent the rest of the summer amid that country's green hills, working out of the little village called Ruyton-of-the-Eleven-Towns.

"There is hardly one town," he wrote the Ma'am, "to say nothing of eleven! What a difference from Sheffield. The air is pure and I ride about with the doctor in his dogcart to see a few patients a day. Even the sick ones are ruddy and fat compared with the healthiest factory worker."

During the wakeful summer nights, Arthur amused himself by working on an imaginative adventure story of the sort that had kept him in tarts at Stonyhurst. He mailed "The Mystery of Sassassa Valley" to *Chambers' Journal*. The editors surprised him by paying three guineas for this simple tale of a demon that turned out to be something quite different. Thus encouraged, he submitted others, but with no more luck that year.

His father's health broke completely during that winter and he was forced to retire. At twenty, Arthur found himself the head of his big family, yet unable to contribute one farthing to their support.

"Even after I graduate, it'll take a long time to build up a decent practice," he complained, but his mother would not let him consider giving up his studies.

Arthur allowed himself two pennies for lunch, the price of a mutton pie, and on occasion another two pennies for a secondhand book. Between studies and reading, he still made time for cricket and rugby. He even squeezed out the price of an occasional gallery seat at the theater.

"But it is humiliating," he told his friend and rugby companion, George Budd, "never to have enough change in your pocket to take a girl out or to buy her a posy from a street vendor!"

"Be more aggressive," roared Budd. "Let them pay the tab, I say, if they want your company."

Arthur had to admit that his big ugly friend seemed to have a way with the ladies—but it was not his way. For him the days of chivalry would never be gone. Only the evening before, Budd had pulled him out of a fight with some soldiers in a theater lobby; he thought they were annoying a pretty girl.

"So there she goes off with them to the nearest pub!" sneered Budd. "Doyle, you're an incurable romantic!"

The summer before his fourth year, Arthur obtained an assistantship with Dr. Reginald Ratcliffe Hoare of Birmingham. Center of the British metal industry, the city was more depressing, if possible, than Sheffield. But Dr. Hoare was a jolly stout fellow with a genial smile. He always dressed gaily in checkered trousers, a bright waistcoat, and a fresh flower in his buttonhole.

"The sight of him walking the smoke-darkened streets makes one feel happy," Arthur wrote his family. "No wonder he has a five-horse practice! He wears out that many horses in a day's work! Dr. Hoare's wife is kindly. . . . They treat me like a son, but the work is incessant. I have long lists of prescriptions to make up each day, for we dispense our own medicine. On the whole, I make few mistakes, though I have been known to send out ointment and pill boxes with elaborate instructions on the lid and nothing at all inside!"

Despite the pressure of work, Arthur continued to write for the magazines. He was intrigued with stories of the American West by Bret Harte, the United States Consul at Glasgow. Frankly imitating Harte, he wrote "An American's Tale," and was encouraged by its prompt sale to the magazine *London Society*.

"But all my writing is secondhand," he complained to his mother. "I need to get out and see the world and have some experiences of my own to write about."

On a dismal afternoon in January, 1880, an opportunity for real adventure came his way. He was in the middle of his fourth year, plugging away diligently in preparation for the midterm examinations, the blight of every student's life. Outside his window, cold, dirty fog made the streets of Edinburgh dark as night. Suddenly a familiar figure appeared out of the mist, hurrying toward his door. Glad of any diversion, Arthur picked up his lamp and hurried down to let the fellow in.

His caller, a medical acquaintance named Currie, blurted out without ceremony: "Would you care to start next week for a whaling cruise? You'd be surgeon, two pounds ten shillings a month plus three shillings oil money."

Arthur's jaw dropped and for a moment he was speechless. Then he asked, "What makes you think I could get such a berth?"

"Because I have it myself," Currie replied promptly. "I find at the last moment that I can't go, and I must get someone to take my place."

"I'll need an Arctic kit?" Arthur questioned.

"You can have mine."

In a little more than a week, Arthur was in the North Sea port of Peterhead. He could hardly believe his good fortune as he stowed his scant belongings beneath his bunk on the two-hundred-ton whaler *Hope*.

4 ◆ Ship's Surgeon

According to Arthur's log, the *Hope* left Peterhead on February 28, 1880, at 2:00 P.M. Immediately the barometer dropped, and the little vessel barely made the two hundred miles to Lerwick, principal harbor in the Shetlands, before a hurricane hit. Even thus sheltered, with masts bare, the wind keeled the *Hope* over on her beam.

"Had we been taken a few hours earlier, we'd have lost our boats surely," Captain John Gray told Arthur as they stood in the sheltered chart room just astern the bridge and gazed out at the angry sea. "And, mon, ye know the boats are the verry life of a whaler!"

Arthur had already discovered that the chief duty of a ship's surgeon was to be a companion to the captain. The situation might have been intolerable had John Gray been a dull or evil man. He was, however, a serious-minded Scot, taciturn and stern on occasion, but always just. Long years at sea had accustomed him to silence, but when he did speak he was worth listening to.

Four days out of Lerwick, Arthur awoke to a bumping sound on the ship's hull. He hurried on deck to find the sea covered with drifting ice, so thick that a man could travel far by jumping from one piece to another.

On one of the swaying ice blocks, Arthur spotted a sleepy seal. The ship moved northward, seeking the seals' breeding grounds. One day they spotted a school of the sleek creatures and took their compass direction. The next morning a shout from the lookout brought everyone up on deck.

The ice ahead appeared to be covered with pepper grains. As the ship inched forward, they turned out to be baby seals, laying like white slugs, almost invisible against the ice except for their little black noses and great dark eyes. They filled the air with half-human cries, so that Arthur felt he was in the middle of a nursery. The roll of the ice in a high wind slid many of the tiny creatures into the water.

On April 3, the open season for seals began; the killing was brutal work.

"I suppose it is no worse than the slaughter-houses where our country's dinner tables are supplied," he wrote the Ma'am. "Yet those glaring crimson pools upon the dazzling white of the icefields, under the peaceful silence of a blue Arctic sky, do seem a horrible intrusion. Still the seals, by their death, help to give a living to a long line of seamen, dockers, tanners, curers, leather merchants and oil-sellers, besides providing the rich with soft fur coats and boots, the scholar with delicate oil for his philosophical instruments."

Arthur had to watch the seal hunt from the *Hope*'s decks, since Captain Gray had forbidden him to leave the ship. Tempest-like winds had set the ice floes rocking and dashing against each other.

"An inexperienced man like yourself would be a care upon the ice," he explained tersely.

In a black temper, Arthur seated himself upon the ice-covered bulwarks. With feet dangling over the water he swayed up and down with the roll of the ship. Suddenly a swell pitched the ship to an acute angle and he shot off into the water. His wrath considerably cooled, he managed to pull himself onto an ice floe and then scrambled back aboard the ship.

"Since you're bound to fall into the water anyhow," the Captain remarked when he found him drying out in the galley, "ye might as well be out on the ice."

Arthur dashed off to join the seal hunt. He justified the Captain's original caution by falling in the sea twice more that day, and finally had to go to bed, since all his clothes were drying in the engine room. Captain Gray gave him the title "Great Northern Diver," which stuck throughout the voyage.

The April sealing was directed against the mothers and their young. In May the ship went further north after the male seals. This was a sporting hunt that Arthur could enjoy, since it took good long-range shooting to bag the wily old seals. In June, the ship traveled north again after whales.

On this cruise, Arthur was an "idler," one who had not signed on to do seaman's work. There were enough "idlers" to man one of the *Hope*'s eight boats. With the steward and two engineers, he manned the oars, while the burly, red-headed cook handled the harpoon, and a strange, dark little man, whom nobody knew, held the rudder.

"It's exciting work," Arthur told the Captain. "The sound of the harpoon gun, the whizzing of the line, the gleam of the great whale's beady eye when it turns on its tormentors, the swish of that great tail when he lashes out in his dying agony—I can see why Herman Melville wrote as he did of the whaling!"

"If ye'll sign on again I can offer ye double pay, as harpooner as well as surgeon," assured Captain Gray.

The offer was tempting. Besides the thrill of the hunt, Arthur loved the peculiar other-world feeling of the Arctic. He wrote:

The memory of the Arctic will haunt me all my life, the perpetual light, the glare of the white ice, the deep blue of the water, and the dry, crisp exhilarating air makes mere living a keen pleasure. There is a feeling of romance in the very loneliness of the Arctic, the sense of living on the very brink of the unknown. . . .

Arthur had gone aboard the whaler a big, gangling youth, but he returned a powerful, full-grown man with a store of health and energy. Before leaving for Edinburgh, he converted his fifty pounds into gold pieces and hid them among his clothes.

"So you can have the fun of looking for them," he told his mother.

In 1881, Arthur passed his final examination with fair though not notable distinction to become a Bachelor of Medicine and Master of Surgery.

At twenty-two, he felt no one would take him seriously as a practitioner of medicine. Yet he was far too restless to continue studying for his doctorate. He wanted to join the Army, the Navy or the Indian Service, anything that would take him abroad yet earn him the experience as well as the money he needed.

He even put his name down with some passenger ship lines, though he had no reason to think an inexperienced doctor could get such a billet. But in September he received a telegram from the African Steam Navigation Company in Liverpool offering him the medical post aboard the *Mayumba*. On October 22, 1881, Dr. Conan Doyle was at sea once more.

The 4000-ton passenger liner seemed a giant after the 200-ton whaler, yet the gales that followed them down to Madeira sent her lurching and staggering. All the passengers were seasick, so there was none of the social life Arthur had looked forward to. A number of ladies, however, found the big, good-looking doctor excellent company when they felt well, as he had been a comfort to them when they were ill.

As they moved south, the heat became intense, and the African coast presented a monotonous line of sand backed by low green bush and an occasional scrawny palm, all bathed in blinding sunlight.

Off Nigeria Arthur caught blackwater fever and lay in his cabin for several days fighting death. There was no one to doctor the doctor, but his rugged constitution finally asserted itself.

Despite tales of human sacrifice, he made several trips inland in a small boat into dark, forbidding mangrove country.

Africa left a deathlike impression on Arthur. He summed up his feelings in his journal: "The sullen brown continent destroys the white man as one might crush nits." And in a little poem:

> Oh Africa, where are the charms
> That sages have seen in thy face?
> Better dwell in Old England on alms
> Than be rich in that terrible place!

In England, it began to look as if the young doctor must indeed exist on alms. Yet he feared one more trip as a ship's surgeon might spoil him for life ashore. He recalled that Dr. Hoare had promised him employment whenever he wished it, so back to Birmingham he went in January, 1882.

The patients Arthur cared for were the poorest or most convalescent. Their homes were unsanitary hovels despite Prime Minister Disraeli's efforts to improve working and living conditions.

"But they all belong to colliery clubs," Arthur wrote the Ma'am. "They pay about a ha' penny a week all year round, well or ill, for which they get medicine and attendance free.

You would think them a poor catch for a doctor, but work in the mines and factories is unhealthy, the living conditions shocking. Since they pay the same in any case, they do not let their ailments go far before they come round to the consulting room. They are my special charges."

The dispensary patients were as homely as their maladies, but their patience and kindness to one another touched young Dr. Doyle. Nearly all of them were coughing their lungs away. The smoke that spewed from factory and foundry carried death in its black depths.

The sight of the children infuriated Arthur. Their thin little bodies were twisted with rickets, and they looked out of hollow eyes at a world that held no joy.

"I want to pack them all off to the country and turn them loose in the fields!" he told Dr. Hoare.

The older man shook his head sadly. "T'would do no good, lad:

> " 'For oh,' say the childen, 'we are weary,
>   And we cannot run or leap;
>   'If we cared for any meadows, it were merely
>   To drop down in them and sleep . . .
>   'For all the day, we drag our burden tiring
>   Through the coal-dark underground;
>   'Or all day, we drive the wheel of iron
>   In the factories, round and round.' "

"I always thought that Elizabeth Barrett Browning overdid the womanly sentiment in 'The Cry of the Children,' " Arthur mused. "Now I see she was being realistic. There certainly should be laws against child labor! Well, anyone who is overstarched might well come here to be unstiffened," he concluded.

Arthur had been in Birmingham only two months when

he received a telegram from his old university friend George Budd. It came from Plymouth and was as exuberant as its sender: "Started here last June. Colossal success. Come down by next train if possible. Plenty of room for you. Splendid opening."

The proposition was tempting, but Arthur knew his friend was a bluffer; he had fled Edinburgh in a cloud of unpaid bills.

"I hesitate to give up a permanent position since they are difficult to find," he wrote Dr. Budd.

Why not call me a liar at once? [Budd wired back] I tell you I saw 30,000 patients last year. They flock to me. Would not cross street to see Queen Victoria. You can have all visiting, surgery, midwifery. Guarantee 300 pounds the first year.

Arthur talked over the offer with Dr. Hoare and his wife that evening at sea.

"I should hate to lose so fine an assistant," Dr. Hoare said. "Still the opportunity appears to be too good to pass up. If it doesn't work out, you know you always have a berth here, my boy."

5. ◆ A Doctor's Statement

Late in the spring of 1882, Dr. Arthur Conan Doyle traveled south to the Channel port of Plymouth. He shared his carriage compartment with a lady and two young people who he assumed were her son and daughter. The girl appeared to be about twenty. Silky light-brown hair framed her pale doll-like face, and she spoke in a soft voice which entranced Arthur.

If ever I do have a settled practice and enough money for matrimony, he thought, picking up his paper to hide his admiring glances, I should think a lovely fragile flower like that would make a fine mate.

The stocky, thick-set boy had little to say, but the two ladies kept up a running commentary on the passing scene. The mother addressed her daughter as "Touie," and Arthur was speculating as to the girl's real name when he was surprised by a sharp kick in the shins from her brother.

Could he be reading my thoughts about his sister? Arthur wondered, moving his legs. But he was kicked again. This could be no accident. He lowered his paper and immediately realized that the boy was ill. His foot was jerking spasmodically, his hands were clenched and drumming against his chest, while his eyes were rolled upward so only the rim of the iris was visible. Arthur grabbed the boy firmly, forcing his head down on the seat and tore open his collar and waist-coat. One flailing heel crashed through the carriage window before he managed to climb astride the lad's knees and get a firm grip on his wrists.

"Don't be alarmed," Arthur cried to the ladies. "It's epilepsy and will soon pass!"

The mother had pulled a bottle out of her bag and offered it to Arthur. "He often has these fits," she told him. "Give him this bromide."

When Arthur glanced up, he noticed the girl was deathly pale. "Your brother is coming around," he cried. And to the mother, "Look to Touie!"

When the young man had recovered they all joined in an animated conversation. The family's name was Hawkins, the girl Louise, her brother Jack. Mrs. Hawkins was a widow. Because of her son's nervous condition they traveled from summer resort to winter resort hoping to benefit him. They were on their way to Plymouth for the bracing sea air. Arthur recommended a vegetable diet for the epileptic, and as they parted he told them hopefully, "Perhaps we shall meet again."

George Budd was waiting on the platform, striding up and down, coattails flying, chin thrust out to show his gleaming teeth. His welcoming roar caused everyone on the platform to stare. He herded Arthur to a handsome carriage drawn by two fine black horses.

"Which house, sir?" asked the coachman tipping his hat.

"Drive to the town residential," ordered Dr. Budd, as he settled back in the well-appointed carriage.

The town residential proved to be more like a small hotel than a private mansion. He also owned a country place and a house in "Doctor's Row" where he practiced, and Arthur wondered how far in debt his friend had gone to purchase them.

Dr. Budd had indeed built up a huge practice. Day after day his waiting rooms were packed, and often the patients spilled over into the courtyard and even into the stable. "Free consultations but pay for your own medicine" brought them in, but his mixture of genius and quackery kept them coming back—and bringing their friends. Most of his income came from the medicine dispensed by his wife. He prescribed amounts enough to kill a horse.

I hope the authorities never have occasion to autopsy one of George's less successful cases! Arthur thought.

Dr. Budd equipped a room for his new partner across from his own, referring to him all surgical and obstetrical cases, or any others he found boring. He even provided Arthur with a brass nameplate which proclaimed that

DR. CONAN DOYLE
Physician and Surgeon

was ready to receive patients.

"No room for the 'Arthur,'" Budd shouted. "More distinguished this way, what?"

So Arthur found himself with a new title, and no use to argue. He certainly could never have afforded so fine a plate!

Dr. Conan Doyle's methods were less flamboyant, but apparently no less successful, than Dr. Budd's. His clientele increased day by day, yet the partnership was short-lived. Two months after Arthur's arrival, Dr. Budd announced that the practice was going to the devil.

"Surely there is always a decrease in illness in midsummer," suggested Arthur.

"T'is you are ruining it," was the blunt reply. "You see, my patients are simple country folk. They come to my door, they see two names, they think 'perhaps we'll be shown to Dr. Doyle instead o' Dr. Budd.' It's me they want to see, so

some cases don't come in at all. That's why the practice is
falling off."

Anger welled up in Arthur. He had come here partly to
oblige an old friend, but he did not have to stay to be in-
sulted. His mother had been right, as usual, when she warned
him against associating with a man she considered "a vulgar
scoundrel—no gentleman at all."

Without a word Arthur stalked out to the stable, picked
up a hammer from the janitor's workbench, and returned to
tear his brass plate from the door.

"There!" he announced to Budd and his startled patients
who were hanging out the windows to watch the doctors
fight. "That won't interfere with you anymore!"

"Come now," soothed Budd, "don't leave in a pet. We'll
talk this over at tea."

Arthur felt there was nothing left to say, but his friend was
conciliatory when they met that evening. "I'm prepared to
stake you a pound a week so you can go into practice for
yourself," Budd offered and Arthur accepted.

To choose a locale, he examined the map for a town similar to Plymouth and settled on Portsmouth. At the end of
July he boarded a coastal steamer with one trunk, which
contained his small wardrobe and the brass nameplate, and
ten pounds in his pocket. He had never considered returning
to his good friend Dr. Hoare in Birmingham. For the first
time in his twenty-three years, he would be completely inde-
pendent!

He found lodgings, then combed every area of Portsmouth
for a suitable location to set up his offices. After a week, he
leased a house in the residential section of Southsea. Number 1 Bush Villas stood between a church and a hotel near
the intersection of Elm Grove and Castle Roads. Arthur
fairly danced through the big empty rooms, from the base-

ment kitchen to the third-floor bedrooms whose windows looked over Southsea toward the Channel.

"My very own house!" he exulted. "But not a stick of furniture to bless it with," he reminded himself, and off he went to an auction he had seen advertised in Portsea, another residential area across the city.

There he picked up three chairs, a table, a piece of carpet for his consulting room, and a bed and mattress—all for four pounds. On the way home, he bought a lamp for his desk "on tick," to be paid for month by month. It had a dark red shade with gold bangles and cost much too much, but Arthur thought he should own one handsome article.

When all his treasures were in place, Dr. Conan Doyle tacked up his nameplate beside the front door. Then he waited.

All dressed up in a frock coat, his silk hat ready and brushed to gleaming, the big mustached man sat behind the flimsy curtain he had hung in his consulting room and watched the passing crowds. It was the height of the summer season in the resort town, and they were headed for the sea-shore, to walk along the parade and sun themselves. A number of people stopped to read his plate, but only out of curiosity.

Accustomed to activity, Arthur grew restless. The stem of his briar pipe was chewed almost through, but he had no extra money for tobacco. Since servants were out of the question, he busied himself by keeping the house clean and cooking light meals. Morning and evening, he slipped out front to sweep the steps and polish the brass plate and door-knob.

When the bell did peal through the empty house, Arthur had an excuse ready for a client—his maid had just stepped out to do an errand. But only peddlers, workmen and beggars disturbed his privacy.

Both Dr. Hoare and Dr. Bell, he remembered, had urged him to continue his studies. "In these days, one cannot go far in medicine without a doctor's degree," the older doctors had warned.

Arthur had introduced himself at the local hospital. Now he availed himself of their small medical library and began preparing for his thesis.

"By concentrated study," he wrote Dr. Bell, "I believe I can pass my M.D. without going to Edinburgh, except for the examinations."

His kind friend replied by sending a suggested course of study and some of his own selected works on medicine and surgery.

One Sunday toward the end of August, Arthur opened his door to find Dr. Hoare standing on the porch. He was carrying a picnic basket laden with Mrs. Hoare's choicest home-cooked goodies. Arthur could not remember when he had been so happy to see anyone. The two friends had a wonderful day touring the waterfront and the fort that guarded the old town. Then Arthur poured out his troubles while stuffing himself with cold roast duck and scones.

"Haven't you eaten since you left Birmingham?" gasped Dr. Hoare as he watched the food vanish.

"Tinned meat and dried fish mostly," admitted Arthur with a grimace of distaste. "I try to spend less than a shilling a day on food."

"Why that's hardly enough to buy your morning kippers! And you need fresh vegetables and fruit," warned Dr. Hoare.

The next evening, Arthur dutifully went to the green-grocer around the corner. Just as he stepped through the door the grocer was seized with an epileptic fit like the one suffered by Jack Hawkins on the train. The young doctor acted quickly to relieve the sufferer. His solicitous treatment was so welcome that the merchant offered him free groceries in return for his services.

As summer passed into fall, the drugs Dr. Conan Doyle had ordered from the Apothecaries' Society stared reproachfully from the dining room mantel where their neat ranks remained unbroken. Only a few stray patients broke the monotony—an anemic old maid who, Arthur guessed, owed every doctor in town and so was forced to consult him; a crusty old army man who admitted to being a walking museum of ailments.

At night, Arthur worked off pent-up energy by walking the miles of esplanade that rimmed the seashore. Often his companion was seventeen-year-old Herbert George Wells, a draper's apprentice with whom he had become friendly when he learned the lad's father was a well-known professional cricketer. Herbert was a diligent reader, and his knowledge of history, philosophy and the sciences was astonishing. He was hopeful of gaining a scholarship to the Royal College of Science.

When not reading for his thesis or tending to his slowly growing practice, Arthur continued to write. Since the publication of "An American's Tale" in 1879, *London Society* had published two more of his stories—"Bones" and "The Gully of Bluemansdyke," both, like the first, frank copies of Bret Harte's western tales. Arthur's stories were set in the wild English colony of New Zealand, but the outlaws still held up wagon trains, in this case carrying gold from the mines. He sprinkled his tales liberally with torture and murder, and the grand finale was the chase by the mounted police, British equivalent of the sheriff's posse or the United States Cavalry.

That fall, Arthur replenished his funds by ten pounds with a sequel to "The Gully of Bluemansdyke" titled "My Friend the Murderer," to appear in the Christmas issue of *London Society*. He laid away the much-needed nest egg for his first quarter's rent, though there were days when he had

not a penny for a stamp. The windfall had come just in time
to save him from defeat.

During the two months in Portsmouth, not one shilling
of the promised aid from Dr. Budd had arrived. Instead one
morning in September, there came an angry letter from his
friend withdrawing the pledge. He wrote:

> When the maid was arranging your room after your de-
> parture, she cleared some pieces of torn paper from under
> the grate. Seeing my name upon them, she brought them to
> her mistress, who pasted them together and found they
> formed a letter from your mother to you, in which I am
> referred to in the vilest terms, such as "swindler" and "un-
> scrupulous Budd.". . .

Certainly Mrs. Doyle had written a number of highly
uncomplimentary letters about her son's former partner, but
Arthur had hidden them all away safely at the bottom of his
trunk, which he now used for a table. Hastily he brushed his
breakfast things aside to open it; the letters were still there!

"The blackguard must have stolen those letters from my
house jacket!" exclaimed Arthur. His honest soul was out-
raged at the idea of Budd and his wife poking around his
room and reading his letters. But that would explain Budd's
strange moody spells and his wife's coolness, as well as the
sudden break in the partnership.

Arthur was thoroughly disillusioned and discouraged. He
might have been tempted to break his lease and once again
take up Dr. Hoare's offer, but in the same mail came a letter
from his mother. Would Arthur take his little brother Innes
for a year? The new baby girl, "Dodo," and little Ida used
up all her strength.

The moment Arthur saw his brother's sandy head and
grinning face at the train window, his spirit rose.

"I've a feeling you're going to bring me luck!" he cried,
enveloping the boy's thin body in a bearish hug.

"I've missed you, Arthur," Innes confided. "All those girls . . . !"

Arthur looked fondly at his brother's freckled face. Except for his thinness, Innes might have been himself as a boy— same patched knickers and worn jacket, and feet that seemed much too big for the rest of him.

Beneath his arm, Innes cradled the handsome clock that was the joy of all the Doyles. Every quarter hour it played an Irish jig, awakening happy echoes of the past. Innes' clattering footsteps on the bare floors, his excited shouts as he proceeded on his journey of discovery through the empty rooms, made Arthur realize how very lonely he had been. He slept on a makeshift bed behind his consulting room, but with bedding sent by the Ma'am he furnished two upstairs bedrooms.

Soon after Innes' arrival, Aunt Annette appeared on the doorstep. The hansom cab that brought her from the station was piled high with a roll of red carpet, a number of paintings and, on the raised seat beside the driver, stood the imposing bust of Grandfather Doyle.

"I smuggled them out of the studio," Annette told her nephews cheerfully. "Your uncles have never forgiven you for not setting up as a Catholic doctor," she reminded Arthur. "They'd help you in that case, you know."

"I cannot be a hypocrite!" He spread his hands in a gesture of helplessness.

Aunt Annette shrugged her ample shoulders and set to work to make the house livable. She sewed curtains for all the front windows, replacing the one dingy pair Arthur had hung in the consulting room. For Innes she made a black jacket, resplendent with brass buttons, so he could serve as the doctor's page when not in school. He shined up the brass, swept the steps and answered the doorbell, which began to

ring more often as 1 Bush Villas took on a more prosperous
look.

In the end, Arthur's own gregarious nature led to success.

"The practice will not come to me," he told Innes impa-
tiently, "so I must go find it. We cannot depend on accidents
occurring at our door or the few newcomers that may drift
our way."

Dr. Conan Doyle became a member of every society in
Portsmouth—literary, social, political or athletic. He played
cricket, attended smokers, even delivered a lecture on the
Arctic before the Literary and Scientific Society. To give
himself confidence, he borrowed from the local taxidermist
every bird and beast that could conceivably inhabit the
Arctic Circle. His audience assumed that he had shot or
trapped the stuffed props, and his reputation as a great
sportsman was assured.

During the summer of 1883, a year after his brother started
practice in Southsea, Innes wrote the Ma'am:

> The patients are crowding in. We have made three bob
> this week. We have vaxenated a baby and got hold of a man
> with consumtion, and to-day a gipsy's cart came up to the
> door selling baskets and chairs so we determined not to let
> the man ring as long as he liked. After he had rong two or
> three times Arthur yelled out at the pitch of his voice, Go a
> way but the man rang again so I went down to the door and
> pulled open the letter box and cried out go a way. The man
> began to swere at me and say that he wanted to see Arthur.
> All this time Arthur thought that the door was open and
> was yelling 'Shut that door.' Then I came upstairs and told
> Arthur what the man had said so Arthur went down and
> opened the door and found out that the gipsy's child had
> measles. . . .

"I ended by giving them the medicine," he added to
Innes' story, "and 5 pence besides—all I had in my pocket.

Many more patients like that and I am ruined!" Arthur
thought his own sudden change from indignant householder
to solicitous physician in hopes of a fee was the most amusing part of the story.

That first year, Dr. Conan Doyle made 154 pounds. When
he sent in his tax return, it was sent back with "most unsat-
isfactory" scrawled across it.

"I entirely agree," Arthur wrote underneath, and returned
the form unchanged. He was immediately summoned to
appear before the assessors with his ledger of accounts. They
could make no sense of it and with much laughter finally
sent him on his way.

By the flickering, rather lurid light of his prized red lamp,
Arthur continued to write. Many of his stories reflected the
sorrow he found around him, the suffering of the hopelessly
crippled, the cruel torments of the insane whom no one
knew how to help, the ever present specter of death. Some of
the stories poked fun at squeamish medical students or at
pompous young doctors who thought themselves wiser than
their elders. The constant wail of the foghorns and hollow
bong of bell buoys in the Channel nearby often set his mind
in weird paths. Few of the stories sold, since popular taste
ran to the sweetly romantic, rather than to realism or horror.

As a mental exercise and vacation from medical realities,
Arthur liked to work out solutions to mysterious occurrences
reported in the newspapers. For years the unexplained dis-
appearance of all passengers and crew from the brig *Mary
Celeste* had intrigued him. On the tenth anniversary, English papers recalled the details.

In December, 1872, the American ship was discovered by
the British brigantine *Dei Gratia* six hundred miles off Portugal near the Azores. She was sailing erratically under jib
and foretopsail, with no man at the wheel. A boarding party
reported finding "all in confusion, the hatches off, ropes

about." The brig's one boat was gone. There was some water
below decks, but the pumps were in order. Despite minute
inspection of the *Mary Celeste* and endless investigations, no
reason for her abandonment was ever discovered.

Mr. Solly Flood, Her Majesty's Advocate-General at Gi-
braltar, summarized official mystification in his report to
the Board of Trade, stating that the *Mary Celeste* had been
found "thoroughly sound, staunch, strong and in every way
seaworthy . . . no appearance of fire or of explosion, or of
alarm . . . or any other assignable cause for abandonment was
discoverable." Other investigators, however, claimed to have
found signs of bloody violence.

These were the details that fired Conan Doyle's imagination and set his pen flying. A Boston doctor named Habakuk
Jephson was cast in the role of lone survivor and teller of
the strange tale. The villain was a pock-marked quadroon
whose experience as a slave had caused him to vow vengeance
on the whole white race. Thereby hung a thrilling epic
which led the reader from an America torn by civil strife
to the bleak, unfriendly shores of Africa's Gold Coast.

"I'll aim high with this one," Arthur told Innes, his ap-
preciative audience of one. "I'm going to send it straight to
James Payn at *Cornhill Magazine*. That's the magazine
Thackeray himself started," he explained. "They publish
only works of literary merit. Robert Louis Stevenson, for
instance, is a regular contributor."

The veteran editor's reply was immediate and heartening
—a check for twenty-nine guineas, dated July 15, 1883. The
brothers stared in disbelief at the slip of paper that represented more money than either had ever seen at one time
before.

"Perhaps Uncle Conan was right," said Innes finally. "Perhaps you'd do better as a storyteller than as a doctor."

6. *Sherlock Holmes Is Born*

"Habakuk Jephson's Statement"—no author's name was given—appeared in the January, 1884, issue of *Cornhill Magazine*. Public reaction to the strange story was at once surprising and encouraging. A telegram to the Central News Agency was published in papers all over England:

> Mr. Solly Flood, Her Majesty's Advocate-General at Gibraltar, pronounces Dr. J. Habakuk Jephson's statement a fabrication from beginning to end.

The telegram was followed by a long report to the government, also published in the papers, denouncing as a menace to international relations the publication of statements of irresponsible people like Dr. Jephson. Many of the so-called facts contained in the account, said Flood, could be officially disproved. The real author roared with delight over the confusion.

"It is certainly a compliment to my fiction to have it accepted as fact!" he told Lottie and Connie, who were with him for a visit before going out to Portugal as governesses. "Edgar Allen Poe pulled off such a hoax, you know. In 1844 he wrote a story for *The New York Sun* reporting the successful crossing of the Atlantic by several Englishmen in a steering balloon."

"Well that was deliberate," reminded Lottie. "You've fooled everyone without even trying!"

"If I could continue to spin yarns that seem so real I should have assured literary fame," Arthur admitted.

But his next stories, like so many he had written before, found no market. He began work on a novel which he titled *The Firm of Girdlestone*.

"For success in the literary world," he told Innes, "one must get one's name on a volume."

That manuscript, too, kept returning to 1 Bush Villas like a homesick pigeon. Arthur confessed he was not surprised.

"It's a perfect hodgepodge of styles, all put together between consultations, vaccinations, operations and deliveries!" He finally threw the dog-eared sheets into the back of a drawer in his old bureau. "I'd best buckle down to finish my doctor's thesis. I'll never make a living spinning yarns."

That fall Innes left for the Richmond Public School in Yorkshire in the north of England near the Scottish border. Arthur preferred to have his brother nearer to him, but the Ma'am insisted on Richmond. Their father was going into a nursing home near there, and she and the younger girls would move to a cottage in the same area.

Without Innes' happy presence, the house seemed intolerably empty. Arthur had rented the basement apartment to an elderly lady, Mrs. Smith, who cooked and cleaned for her keep. But conversation was not her strong point. Arthur went out as much as his work allowed.

He distinguished himself in the local football league, won a cigar case for his skill at bowls. Occasionally, he admitted only in letters to Lottie, he "got drunk as an owl."

Early one morning in March, 1885, a neighbor, Dr. Pike, came knocking on Arthur's door. He was just returning from a visit to a young patient whose symptoms were disquieting.

"I'd appreciate it if you'd step around with me and have a look at him," Dr. Pike asked.

Arthur finished quickly with the patients in his waiting room, then shrugged into his greatcoat. A frosty, moisture-laden wind whipped off the Channel as the doctors hurried up Castle Road toward the seaside parade.

"The mother of this lad is a widow from Gloucestershire," Dr. Pike explained breathlessly. "The boy has been a chronic sufferer from epileptic fits so the three—there is a daughter, too—travel from watering place to watering place. Ordinarily they would be on the Riviera now, but for young Jack's being taken ill."

Something familiar about the description of the family prompted Arthur to ask, "What did you say the name was?"

"I didn't say, but it's Hawkins. Ah, here we are."

The house Dr. Pike had turned to was a typical low-priced boardinghouse of the sort that lined the parade and whose only virtue was a view of the esplanade along the water.

"I believe I have met this family," Arthur said as they waited for an answer to their ring. "Is the young lady's name Louise?"

"The mother uses a pet name that sounds like 'Touie.' "

"The very ones!" cried Arthur. "I met them on a train four years ago. I doubt they'll remember me."

The moment they entered the sedate, high-ceilinged room where Jack Hawkins lay, Arthur knew this was the lad he had treated on the train to Plymouth. The mother and daughter, both pale and drawn, stood silently by the window as Dr. Pike introduced his colleague. They showed no signs of recognition.

Dr. Conan Doyle turned quickly to the patient. A brief examination showed that he had been consulted only as a gesture. The stocky boy he remembered was now thin and wasted. He had cerebral meningitis, an illness that was usually fatal.

"Jack has violent attacks when his fever is up," Mrs. Hawkins told the two doctors as she followed them out of the sick room. "It disturbs our hosts and they would like us to leave. But where could we take poor Jack? To put him in a hospital is unthinkable!" The tall, dignified lady threw up her hands in a gesture of helplessness that wrung Arthur's heart.

Both doctors knew the average hospital to be crowded and unsanitary, the last place on earth they would send a very ill patient. Arthur looked past Mrs. Hawkins' drooping figure to the pale brown-haired girl standing by the window, weeping quietly.

"Surely we can work out a solution," he assured Mrs. Hawkins. "I must confer with Dr. Pike. We will be in touch with you by evening."

"That young man needs constant care." Dr. Conan Doyle started reviewing the case the moment the door closed behind them. "Yet, should he live long, such care may so run down the ladies that they too may become ill."

"Quite so," agreed Dr. Pike.

"If you approve, I shall have Mrs. Smith fix up my brother's bedroom, so I can take him in as a resident patient."

"My boy," cried Dr. Pike, "I hoped you would offer. Were my wife not so ill, I'd have done it long since myself!"

The following afternoon, they bundled Jack Hawkins in rugs and moved him in a rolling chair to 1 Bush Villas. Despite all precautions and the shortness of the journey, the exertion and the cold made him worse. By evening his temperature soared, his face was flushed and he muttered and flung his arms about wildly. Arthur gave him the prescribed dose of chloral, a strong sedative, and his patient finally dropped off into a deep sleep. Leaving a low flame in a hurricane lamp to serve as a night light, he retired to the next room.

Toward daybreak a loud crash brought Arthur out of bed and into the next room. His patient was standing beside the bed, his eyes wild in the flickering lantern light. Around him were strewn bits of broken crockery. Evidently, in trying to climb out of bed, he had knocked over the heavy bowl and pitcher that stood on the washstand. Arthur picked him up as if he were a child and tucked him back under the covers. Then he settled down in the chair beside his charge to watch through the cold predawn until Mrs. Smith appeared with the lad's arrowroot tea.

Despite all the doctors could do, Jack Hawkins died the next day. Arthur made it his special duty to console Mrs. Hawkins and her daughter. The attraction he had felt for Touie four years before burgeoned into a passionate desire to win her love. Her wide blue-green eyes enthralled him. Daily visits, at first made on the pretext of professional concern, became a habit.

Touie proved a perfect companion. She was happy to enjoy what he enjoyed—a walk along the beach, a concert or play, a quiet evening beside the fire while he read aloud or confided his hopes and dreams. Mrs. Hawkins, bent silently to her needlework, remained pleasantly in the background.

One evening Arthur pretended to go into a trance. "I see a railroad carriage," he droned. "I see a tall handsome lady with ostrich feathers in a green hat. I see a lovely young girl in blue. . . ."

"Oh, Mama!" Touie cried delightedly. "I told you he was the one in the train that day!"

She had jumped up in her excitement. Her face was becomingly flushed, her lips softly parted. Arthur had all he could do to keep from taking her in his arms.

When his mother came down for a visit that May, he told her he had asked Miss Hawkins to marry him.

The Ma'am had seen Arthur in and out of love a dozen times, but after meeting Touie, she gave her blessing at once. "She is exactly right for you, son."

Arthur Conan Doyle married Louise Hawkins on August 6, 1885, and they moved into the snug upstairs apartment he had prepared at 1 Bush Villas. There was red plush furniture and a piano for Touie, which he bought on the hire-purchase system. His bachelor days were over, and he did not regret leaving them for an instant. At twenty-six he was ready to settle down. Marriage, in fact, agreed with him. The increased responsibility and regular life seemed to expand his mind and spirit.

A month before his marriage, he had received his doctorate from Edinburgh. With that out of the way, the thoughts and plots of stories long held back crowded in upon him. He began to write more enthusiastically than ever before. *Cornhill* accepted two more stories that year—"John Huxford's Hiatus," a drama about an amnesia victim, and "The Ring of Thoth," a weird tale of Egyptology and eternal life. The Scotch magazine *Blackwood* bought "The Physiologist's Wife," the story of a professor who died of a broken heart. All of them showed a fine craftsmanship developed through much practice and an innate feeling for and understanding of people. Much of his material came from his growing mound of notebooks, in which he recorded his thoughts and impressions of people and events.

"Now I think I could try something more ambitious," Arthur told Touie as they sat before the fire one winter's evening. 'Something crisper, fresher, more workman-like."

Touie remonstrated that she felt everything her beloved Arthur wrote was crisp, fresh, workman-like and altogether wonderful. Her husband jumped up from his chair to give her a bearlike hug that almost toppled her off her own chair.

"No, but look how Émile Gaboriau dovetails his plots," he pointed out, pacing up and down the little sitting room. He had been rereading the French master of mystery aloud to Touie. "Yet Mr. Poe's detective, M. Dupin, and Gaboriau's LeCoq seem to me a little contrived, like puppets. Now if one could create a sleuth who seemed made of flesh and blood. . . . By jove, m'love, you'd stop your infernal scale running with every young hopeful in the town and play only for my pleasure and your own!'

"Now, Arthur, you worry too much," soothed Touie. "I like giving piano lessons. I enjoy the children."

"Well I have made less than three hundred pounds at my practice this year," her husband pointed out, "and doubt if I'll ever make much more—in Southsea, at any rate."

"With my little income and Mama's, we are quite comfortable."

"We are divinely comfortable, beloved," cried Arthur. "If I had a million pounds I could not be happier!"

Yet the idea of creating a living, breathing detective piqued his fancy. It would not be enough to say that such a character did this or that.

"One must give examples of his methods of scientific detection," he told himself.

The hawklike face of his Edinburgh professor, Joseph Bell, grew larger and larger in his mind. Arthur could almost hear the high-pitched nasal voice as the surgeon gleefully explained his eerie trick of spotting details to a wide-mouthed wondering class.

"The trained eye, gentlemen, a simple matter," Dr. Bell insisted. "Now this man is a left-handed cobbler." Dramatic pause. "Observe the worn places on the corduroy britches where a cobbler rests his lapstone? The right-hand side, you'll note, is far more worn than the left. He uses his left-hand for hammering the leather."

Dr. Bell's sharp gray eyes seemed to gleam triumphantly in the gloom of Conan Doyle's consulting room. Visiting hours were over, but the doctor still sat brooding at his desk. Upstairs Touie ran through the scales with a late pupil.

"And this man is a French polisher-r-r," the broad Scots' accent rumbled through Arthur's memory. "Can't you smell-l-l him? From close observation and deduction, gentlemen, it is possible to make a diagnosis that will be correct in any and every case. . . ."

"Are you asleep, Arthur?" Touie stood in the doorway. "Your tea is ready."

"I have him, m'love, I have my man," he jumped up waving a sheaf of scribbled notes. "Even his name will distinguish him from the Mr. Sharps and Mr. Ferrets of ordinary detective fiction.

"A completely English gentleman," he continued over tea, "but eccentric. A philosopher—perhaps a collector of violins—" He thought a moment. "What do you think of 'Holmes' for a name?"

"Make his first name Sherrinford," put in Touie excitedly. "That's such a lovely name."

Arthur jotted it down and studied it a moment. "No. Too fancy," was his judgment. "More suitable for the hero of a romantic novel than for the intellectual and slightly bohemian character I have in mind. But it's close, my dear. Let me see . . . Sherlock, perhaps?"

"That sounds very Irish. . . ."

"I could give him Irish ancestors like myself. Sherlock Holmes. It has a ring, don't you think? Yes. I believe Mr. Sherlock Holmes will do very nicely."

7 ◆ Sherlock Holmes Takes the Stage

Winter winds off the Channel flung salt-laden rain against the window panes of Southsea. Fog crept up the estuary to shroud the streets of the deserted resort. Only the mournful "bong" of the channel buoys accompanied Dr. Conan Doyle—and the wraithlike figment of his imaginings —as he hurried on his rounds.

During the first two months of 1886, Conan Doyle turned over in his mind the idea of a scientific detective who would solve cases entirely through his own powers of observation and reasoning. Out of his musings emerged the gaunt figure of Sherlock Holmes. His very appearance must attract attention, Arthur decided.

Tall and lean, with a hawklike nose and piercing eyes, he would give an immediate impression of an eager wolfhound on scent. A square prominent chin would indicate determination. Long white surgeon's fingers would imply extraordinary delicacy of touch.

"A caricature of dear old Dr. Bell," chuckled Arthur to himself. "I hope he won't object."

But could he reproduce the analytical mind? Could he create the circumstances of a crime, then deduce the solution? Even Dr. Bell sometimes erred when all the facts were presented. The pursuit of a criminal must be reduced to an exact science. Yet no system of scientific criminology existed.

"Very well then, I will create one," Arthur told the bust of his grandfather that peered down at him from the top of the bookcase. "The study of footprints, mud, dust—the use of chemistry, anatomy, psychology—the tools of a good doctor. Why not?"

"Sherlock Holmes must have a companion, Touie," he told his wife. "Someone to record the great sleuth's cases—give the clues, ask the questions. He would always be skeptical, even a little dense, about Holmes' theories and deductions, so the detective would have to explain all his conclusions."

"An impersonation of Mr. John Q. Public?" asked Touie.

Arthur looked at her thoughtfully. "Yes, John—a thoroughly British character, solid and literal-minded where Holmes is eccentric and given to flights of fancy, but intelligent enough to understand and appreciate his friend's remarkable gifts. I think of a man like our own Dr. James Watson here in Portsmouth—a man of wide interests and insatiable curiosity. I have told you how he embarrasses some lecturers at the Literary and Scientific Society with his searching questions."

Dr. John Watson emerged from Conan Doyle's imagination looking very much like his creator. As "the reminiscenses of John H. Watson, M.D.," began, the bluff mustached army surgeon had been wounded in the second Afghan war and invalided home. In the chemical laboratory of the London University Hospital, he meets the strange man who is to govern the course of his life.

This was a lofty chamber, lined and littered with countless bottles. Broad, low tables were scattered about, which bristled with retorts. There was only one student in the room, who was bending over a distant table absorbed in his work. At the sound of our steps he glanced around and sprang to his feet with a cry of pleasure. "I've found it! I've found it," he shouted . . . running towards us with a test-tube in his hand. "I have found a re-agent which is precipitated by haemoglobin, and by nothing else." Had he discovered a gold mine, greater delight could not have shone upon his features.

"Dr. Watson, Mr. Sherlock Holmes. . . ."

"How are you?" he said cordially, gripping my hand with a strength for which I should hardly have given him credit. "You have been in Afghanistan, I perceive."

"How on earth did you know that?" I asked in astonishment.

"Never mind," said he, chuckling to himself. "The question now is about haemoglobin. No doubt you see the significance of this discovery of mine?"

"It is interesting, chemically, no doubt," I answered, "but practically . . ."

"Why, man, it is the most practical medico-legal discovery for years. Don't you see that it gives us an infallible test for blood stains?"

The building of a plot, the weighing of evidence and the sequence of events were more difficult for Conan Doyle than the building of character and mood. But when he began to write, the work went quickly.

He conceived the perfect setting for his sleuth to be the great cesspool of crime that lay stagnant behind the proper gray façade of London—not modern London, but the mysterious city of his youth. He saw his hero loping through gas-lit streets on whose wet pavements the shadowy mud-splattered cabs made no sound. He walked again in Baker Street where the glassy eyes of Mme. Tussaud's murderers peered down on him.

The working title for the first story was "A Tangled Skein." It led Holmes and Watson up a yellow path through a drooping garden into a deserted house, to find on the floor of the drawing room a "grim, motionless figure . . . with vacant, sightless eyes staring up at the discoloured ceiling." The silence of the empty house was loud with the splatter of raindrops against the dirty windowpanes. The "vulgar, flaring wallpaper . . . was blotched with mildew." One flickering finger of light from a red-wax candle pointed to the word RACHE, which was scrawled across the wall in dripping, blood-red letters. . . .

Conan Doyle retitled his novelette *A Study in Scarlet* and sent it off to James Payn of the popular *Cornhill Magazine*. He knew the book, which ran to about two hundred pages, was as good as he could make it.

It was a windy Sunday in late April. Outside there was the fresh damp smell of spring. Bright sunshine warmed the cluttered sitting room where the newlyweds were enjoying unusual leisure.

". . . alone in our glory," Touie wrote Lottie in faraway Portugal, "since Mama and Mrs. Smith have gone to church."

Such moments were rare for the busy doctor and his bride. Besides the demands of his growing practice, his writing, his clubs and sports, Arthur spent an increasing number of hours at the Portsmouth Eye Hospital. The correction of seeing defects and the treatment of eye maladies was a growing field of medicine that intrigued him. Meanwhile Touie's understanding nature had attracted a whole new group of friends who knew they could depend on her ready sympathy at any hour.

To top it all, Dr. Conan Doyle had launched himself into the troubled political world. The issue that aroused him was the Irish nationalist movement for home rule—Ireland's demand for self-government and independence from England. Loyal Fenian men of Ireland drew attention to their cause by placing dynamite in strategic spots around London. Sixteen sticks of it were found beneath the Nelson Monument in Trafalgar Square. Minor explosions occurred in the offices of the London *Times,* in the Tower of London, at Victoria Station and in the House of Commons. Someone even planted dynamite in a lavatory at Scotland Yard, blowing out the side of the building.

Conan Doyle was a liberal, and despite Irish blood on both sides of his family, he opposed home rule vigorously.

"Ireland is part of Britain," he insisted. "England and Ireland are wedded together with the sapphire wedding-ring of the sea," he told a rally of anti-home-rulers, "and what God has placed together let no man pluck asunder!"

"Did I say that!" he cried when he saw the newspaper account of his speech. "Public speaking is certainly not one of my strong points!"

"I thought you were magnificent," Touie assured him, "and so did everyone else."

Touie had taken advantage of her husband's frequent absences to embroider slippers for his twenty-seventh birthday present. Mrs. Hawkins gave him new cricket gloves. Then they led him to the third floor where they had outfitted a study with a huge oak desk, bookcases, a leather easy chair. Arthur was completely surprised.

"How did you manage to get all the furnishings in without my seeing?" he exclaimed.

"You had to have a place to write," Touie told him. "There are too many interruptions down in the office."

"You may only be encouraging me in a wasteful folly," Arthur reminded her. "My poor little *Study* seems to be no more desirable than *Girdlestone.*"

Arthur had become resigned to the rejections of *The Firm of Girdlestone,* but when *A Study in Scarlet* began making the same rounds, he was disheartened. Payn at *Cornhill* had found the story "capital," but he wrote: "It's too long—and too short—for *Cornhill Magazine*."

Conan Doyle sent the manuscript to Arrowsmith of Bristol, then to Frederick Warne and Co. Both returned it so fast that Arthur wrote to his mother in Yorkshire:

"My poor *Study* has never even been read by anyone except Payn. Verily literature is a difficult oyster to open."

Refusing to give up, he mailed it next to Ward, Lock and Company. There the chief editor, Professor G. T. Bettany, gave the book to his wife for judgment. A writer herself, Mrs. Bettany was enthusiastic about it.

"This man is a born novelist!" she told her husband. "The book will be a great success."

In accepting Arthur's *A Study in Scarlet,* Ward, Lock and Company communicated none of the lady's enthusiasm however. They wrote:

Dear Sir:
  We have read your story and are pleased with it. We could not publish it this year as the market is flooded at present with cheap fiction, but if you do not object to its being held over till next year, we will give you £ 25 for the copyright.
                                Yours faithfully,
                                Ward, Lock & Co.
  Oct. 30, 1886

"Now there's a tempting offer!" cried Arthur, throwing the letter down on the breakfast table in disgust. Touie picked it up and read it.

"Why it's positively insulting! 'Cheap fiction' indeed!"

"Poor as I am, I hesitate to accept that—nor will I without a fight!" Arthur decided. "Sherlock Holmes may become popular, and without the copyright I'd get not one penny for reprints."

Conan Doyle wrote Ward, Lock suggesting the sale be on a royalty basis. The reply was a decided negative:

> . . . we shall be unable to allow you to retain a percentage on the sale of your work as it might give rise to confusion. The tale may be inserted together with some others, in one of our annuals.

He sold *A Study in Scarlet* outright for twenty-five pounds. "With luck it may get my name before the public," Arthur told his family philosophically. He had already turned his mind to an ambitious historical work that he felt would test his powers to the full.

Below his study windows, history blended with the present. New torpedo boats flew up the estuary past the old *Victory*, Nelson's flagship at the Battle of Trafalgar. Elizabethan culverins, the long cannon of the sixteenth century, lined the walks that led to the forts, now armed with modern artillery. In the streets of Portsmouth, as elsewhere in England, the Puritans or "Roundheads" had fought the King's Cavaliers in the bitter civil and religious wars that had ushered in freedom and constitutional government.

Into those streets, Conan Doyle introduced big-boned Micah Clarke, son of Ironside Joe Clarke, once pikeman for the Puritan leader Oliver Cromwell. Beneath familiar elms, he placed the Royal Horse Guard Blues, rolling their dice while they waited for a rebellion to put down or a war to fight. Out of the sea emerged the villainous Decimus Saxon with his drooping eyelid, his whining voice.

Conan Doyle mingled imagination and a lusty sense of humor with astonishing factual detail to create a sweeping saga of Puritan life in Anglican England. The somber fighters with their Bibles and broadswords, the lounging court fops, the dashing Cavaliers—all assumed flesh and blood dimensions as they strutted across the pages of *Micah Clarke*.

While still at work on his historical novel, *A Study in Scarlet* together with two drawing-room plays appeared in *Beeton's Christmas Annual of 1887* in London, New York and Melbourne. No critic troubled to review it.

When the issue sold out, Ward, Lock decided to publish *A Study in Scarlet* by itself. Arthur could not earn a penny from the reprint. He did, however, persuade the publishers to allow his father to do the illustrations.

"The knowledge that his work is still wanted in London has given your father new life," wrote the Ma'am.

Charles Doyle produced six black-and-white sketches, showing three different concepts of Sherlock Holmes. Only one resembled his son's description—the youthful, exultant Holmes in the chemical laboratory of the University of London Hospital, at the moment he meets Dr. Watson.

Early in 1888, Conan Doyle finished *Micah Clarke* and mailed it to *Cornhill Magazine*. Arthur wrote Lottie:

> If it comes off, we may, I think, take it as proved that I can live by my pen. I should go to London to study the eye. I should then go to Berlin and study the eye. I should then go to Paris and study the eye. Having learned all there is to know about the eye, I should come back to London and start as an eye-surgeon, still, of course, keeping literature as my milk-cow.

Editor Payn scotched Dr. Conan Doyle's dreams. "How," he asked, "can you waste your time and your wits writing historical novels?"

Other reactions to his major literary effort almost discouraged Arthur. *Micah Clarke* went from publisher to publisher until, in November, 1888, Andrew Lang of Longman's accepted it. Jubilant, Conan Doyle hurried up to London to lunch at the Saville with that noted representative of one of England's finest old publishing houses.

"Our brindle-haired Scotch angel is enthusiastic about big Micah!" Arthur told Touie that evening. "The editors wish to publish as soon as possible."

Touie beamed proudly at him from her big chair by the fire. Her thin little face and slender body had grown round and plump in the past few months. She was expecting a baby very soon, and the experience had given her a healthy radiance that made her almost beautiful. Arthur lifted her gently and carried her to their big, canopied bed.

"We can have a betting pool," he told her as he tucked her under the fluffy feather counterpane, "as to which shall appear first—the baby or the book."

Dr. Conan Doyle had assisted cradles full of babies into the world. He had labored and brought forth literary works. Creation was no mystery to him. But, on the cold morning in late January, 1889, when he held the squirming mite that was his own daughter, he was filled with wonder. The child would be named for his mother and Touie.

"Mary Louise Conan Doyle!" he announced. "A perfect physical specimen." He handed the baby to the midwife to be washed and dressed. "And with those lungs, she'll always make herself heard," he assured his drowsy young wife.

Micah Clarke, published in late February, was hailed by the literary world. Touie pasted review after review into a leather-bound scrapbook, while her husband turned over in his mind a score of new ideas. Whatever else he did, now he knew he must write.

Meanwhile, across the Atlantic, *A Study in Scarlet* had attracted more attention than in his native England. To Americans, Mr. Sherlock Holmes was the very model of an English gentleman detective. Much of the story was laid in the western plains of America during pioneer days.

In Philadelphia, Mr. Stoddart, an editor of J. B. Lippincott Company, Publishers, was preparing to leave for London to commission several stories.

"Find this A. Conan Doyle, or Dr. Watson, or whoever it is that writes the Sherlock Holmes mysteries," his chief instructed. "Get him to write another for us. The man has a real talent for storytelling."

8. *Exit Dr. Conan Doyle*

At Eastertime of 1889, Dr. Conan Doyle accompanied some friends to the New Forest for a brief holiday. The extensive area of woodland and heath had been enclosed as a hunting preserve by William the Conqueror and was still an unspoiled vacation spot. With his deep sense of history, Arthur could almost hear the jangling armor of the knights who once rode along the paths he walked, and the hearty banter of the bowmen.

That summer he returned with a cart full of books on the Middle Ages and shut himself up in a friend's cottage until autumn to begin work on another historical novel which he called *The White Company*. Beneath the crudeness of that faraway time, he found the roots of chivalry which ruled his own life.

"Fearless to the strong; humble to the weak—chivalry towards all women of high or low degree. Help to the helpless. . . . To this I pledge my knightly sword."

"Oh, Arthur!" cried Touie when she saw the mound of closely written notebooks he brought home. "How will you ever make a book from all that?"

To Conan Doyle, the knights who served under the banner of the Royal Plantagenets, and the bowmen they led, were like old friends. What they did, he would have done; what they believed, he believed. There was little Sir Nigel Loring, leader of *The White Company*, soft-voiced, gentle and absolutely fearless. His squire, Alleyne Edricson, both student and soldier, would ride on any venture, suffer any hardship, to right a wrong. They led a fearsome army of steel-capped archers—men like Samkin Aylward, whose arrow could split a wooden peg at 150 paces, and Big John Hordle who could wrestle any man to the ground.

"We are free Englishmen!" shouts Aylward. . . .

"Arthur?" Touie stood hesitant just outside the door of his blue-walled study. "I hate to disturb you, but there's a telegram from London."

"Come in, my love, come in." Arthur forced his mind back to the present. "Let's see. It's from a Mr. Stoddart of the publishing house of Lippincott in Philadelphia. He asks me to dine in London on Tuesday next."

Conan Doyle found Stoddart an excellent conversationalist. Another guest was Oscar Wilde, who was already well-known as a writer.

"Ah, Dr. Doyle!" Wilde greeted Arthur like an old friend. "I've had the pleasure of reading your *Micah Clarke*. A great book, beautifully written, tremendous detail!"

Arthur considered Oscar Wilde an artist who towered above his contemporaries. Praise from such a source was a rare compliment.

Mr. Stoddart commissioned both Oscar Wilde and Conan Doyle to write short novels for *Lippincott's Magazine*. Wilde's contribution was *The Picture of Dorian Gray*. Conan Doyle's *The Sign of the Four* appeared first in February, 1890. In it Sherlock Holmes had already become a noted detective. His practice, he boasts to Dr. Watson, has extended to the Continent. He has authored several papers on new methods of scientific crime detection which are being translated into French. The detective explains:

> "They are all upon technical subjects. Here, for example, is one 'Upon the Distinction between the Ashes of the various Tobaccos.' In it I enumerate a hundred and forty forms of cigar, cigarette, and pipe tobacco, with coloured plates illustrating the difference in the ash. It is a point which is continually turning up in criminal trials.
>
> ". . . Here is my monograph upon the tracing of footsteps, with some remarks upon the uses of plaster of Paris as a preserver of impresses. Here, too, is a curious little work upon the influence of a trade upon the form of the hand. . . ."

No textbook on "modern" methods of crime detection had been published in 1890. The scientific ideas introduced by Conan Doyle in the two Holmes novels were truly innovations. A Philadelphia tobacconist wrote Sherlock Holmes to ask how he could obtain a copy of the monograph on tobacco ash. It was the first of many fan letters addressed to the "unofficial consulting detective . . . the only one in the world."

The second appearance of *The Sign of the Four* was in book form in London that same year under the imprint of Spencer Blackett. The one illustration, done by Charles Kerr, showed the Holmes that Conan Doyle had envisioned —tall, hawk-faced, with the wide bulging forehead indicative of unusual brain development. Unfortunately the drawing was made ridiculous by an oversized beak.

". . . and poor Dr. Watson is made to appear a bushy-whiskered idiot!" laughed the author.

The Sign of the Four had little more success in England than *A Study in Scarlet*. Conan Doyle could not have cared less. High above the streets of Portsmouth, he was listening to the trumpets of *The White Company*. The story enthralled him. By July, the long work was completed. As he wrote the last words, he felt a thrill of exultation.

"That's done it!" he cried, hurling his inky pen across the room where it made an ugly black smudge on the blue wallpaper.

On the floor below, Mary Louise was awakened from her nap by her father's roar, and started to whimper.

"What is it, Arthur?" Touie ran up the attic steps, breathless and alarmed.

"There is a book that will live!" he declared, lovingly patting the towering sheaf of manuscript. "Not only does it illuminate our national tradition, but it's a bang-up good adventure story, as well!"

Though he knew James Payn disliked historical novels in general, he gave him the first reading of *The White Company*. "It is the best historical novel since *Ivanhoe*," pronounced the editor in accepting it to run serially in *Cornhill Magazine*.

Conan Doyle should have been elated by Payn's reaction; now that his big project was out of the way, he could relax. Instead, he became as jumpy and restless as a racehorse at the barrier. He went about his medical duties without enthusiasm. His sports and clubs palled; no new ideas for stories excited him.

His patients and family knew him as a big, hearty fellow, ruddy-faced, bushy-whiskered, dependable. Apparently he had not a nerve in his body. However, a body that housed so dynamic a mind and spirit must operate on a high-strung nervous system. That system had been hard-pushed for many months!

He brooded too over the untimely death of his sister Annette in faraway Portugal. She had contracted smallpox a few months before and was gone before any member of her family even knew she was ill. Arthur was haunted by the memory of her earnest face, always too serious for one so young, and of her pretty head with its crown of chestnut hair bent everlastingly to her books. Could so much goodness and beauty have vanished into the alien earth, leaving no trace? What of that sweet, unselfish spirit?

In his grief, his mind refused to accept the finality of death. More and more he thought about the existence of life after death, even though it was in opposition to all scientific knowledge.

He found a possible answer in spiritualism, a belief that the human personality continues to exist after death and can communicate with the living through the agency of a medium. The advocates of spiritualism believe that death merely means a change of wave length for those who die, and the medium is said to be able to receive radiations which cannot be sensed by an ordinary person.

One of Arthur's patients, General Drayson, a distinguished astronomer and mathematician, spoke often of his conversion to spiritualism.

"The existence of life after death is a fact that can be proved," he insisted. "I have spoken many times with my dead brother. You can do the same."

The possibility of proof fired Arthur's curiosity, and he accepted the General's invitation to sit in on a spiritualist seance.

The group sat around a dining room table, with their hands resting upon it. Suddenly the heavy piece of furniture began to sway, rose a little, then tapped with one leg. Through a medium, people asked questions addressed to relatives or friends who had passed on. The table taps seemed to spell out alphabetical replies.

Arthur was certain his companions must be pushing the table. Since he never doubted the power of the mind, he thought it possible that they willed the table leg to tap the proper number of times.

With Mr. Ball, a well-known architect, he conducted a number of successful experiments in thought transference. Sitting behind his friend, Dr. Conan Doyle drew a diagram. Repeatedly Mr. Ball made approximately the same figure.

"This proves that I can convey my thought without words," Arthur declared. "If such a conclusion can be verified at six feet, why not at a distance? And if thought can travel a distance to produce a perceptible effect, then one must conclude that the excretion of the brain differs entirely from any purely physical material!"

"So," observed General Drayson, "you have proved to your own satisfaction that substance other than the purely physical does exist. It is only another step to accept spiritualistic manifestations. Why, the ectoplasm which surrounds a spirit can be actually photographed."

Conan Doyle was not yet ready to concede so much, but in his list of "books to be read" that year he included seventy-four psychic works. Meanwhile more immediate problems plagued him.

He had been eight years at Southsea and built up a reasonable practice. With the publication of the two big historical novels and the two Holmes novelettes, his previously rejected short stories and even *The Firm of Girdlestone* were suddenly in demand.

"And what has it all got me but a few hundred pounds in savings!" he grumbled.

The few hundred pounds, however, enabled him to go to Berlin in October to see the famous Dr. Robert Koch demonstrate a supposed cure for tuberculosis.

"I have no faith in this cure," Arthur told Touie, "but I have a great urge to see the demonstration."

His curiosity was that of a reporter rather than a medical

man. Dr. Koch's cure was so widely publicized that thousands of sufferers were flocking to Berlin. Many were dying on the train. Arthur found the cure was greatly overrated, as he had suspected, and he returned to write a warning for the *Review of Reviews* against overoptimism.

But a change took place in Dr. Conan Doyle as a result of his trip. On the Continental Express going to Berlin he met a distinguished London physician named Malcolm Morris. As the train pounded across darkened Europe, the two men talked through the night.

"I was once a provincial doctor like yourself," Morris said. "It was a blind alley. I went up to London as a skin specialist and have made quite a hit in Harley Street."

"I have thought something of specializing in eye work," Arthur confided. "I have worked a good deal at the Portsmouth Eye Hospital."

"Why not spend six months in Vienna studying the eye," suggested Dr. Morris, "then set up practice in London. You would have a nice clean life with plenty of leisure for your writing."

Arthur put the proposition to Touie one November evening as they sat before the fire. She looked up from her needlework in surprise.

"When should we go, Arthur?"

"Now. Immediately."

Most of the furniture had to be sold. However, the bust of Grandfather Doyle, the pictures and vases, even the worn red stair carpet were carefully packed for storage.

"Let me keep the musical clock with me," begged Mother Hawkins. "I've grown accustomed to a lively tune each quarter hour. T'will be company for me and amuse the child."

Mary Louise had grown chubby and walked quite well on her fat bandy legs, if someone held her sash. Now nearly two,

her round face was doll-like with its bright blue eyes and
frame of golden ringlets.

"I hope you and the nursemaid can manage with her in
rooms," Touie worried.

"I managed you and your brother in rooms for many
years," her mother reminded her.

"We'll not be gone long, in any case," Arthur soothed.

If he had any regrets about leaving Southsea they were
overridden by anticipation. The eight years at Portsmouth
had been eventful years of growth and change, but now his
overpowering urge was to move forward. So much time had
been spent in writing that his practice had dwindled to almost nothing.

As the day of departure approached, friends and patients
crowded to 1 Bush Villas to wish him well, and the Portsmouth Literary and Scientific Society, of which he was
secretary, gave him a farewell dinner.

The lectures that Arthur attended at the Krankenhaus in
Vienna proved to be a total loss. His rusty conversational
German was worthless when confronted with medical tech-
nicalities. But he and Touie enjoyed the gay Viennese society, and Arthur had some excellent skating. To cover
expenses, he wrote a light novel titled *The Doings of Raffles
Haw*.

On the way back to England, the Doyles visited Paris.
There Arthur spent a few days observing Dr. Landolt, the
famous French oculist. Because of his perfect knowledge of
French, those days were worth all the weeks in Vienna.

It was a joy to be in Paris again, and to show Touie all
the well-remembered haunts of his youth. Together they
stood outside the wall of the familiar garden on the Avenue
Wagram. Dear Uncle Michael and Aunt Susan had died
many years before. The fragrance of the new spring buds on

the chestnut tree that hung over the wall filled Arthur with longing for the days spent beneath that very tree.

By April they were back in London and reunion with little Mary Louise and Mother Hawkins.

"We were so lonesome without you," cried Touie, hugging them both. It seemed her baby was all grown up in three months. "I'll never leave you again," she vowed.

The Conan Doyles took lodgings in Montague Place, in London, with doctor's quarters close by at 2 Devonshire Place. Arthur's consulting room was at the front of the house, and he had part use of a waiting room.

"But it looks as though both are waiting rooms," he told Touie after a week passed without a single patient.

As Dr. Conan Doyle walked each morning from Montague Place to his offices, unmedical thoughts churned uppermost in his mind. Homeward-bound from Paris, he had run through a number of popular magazines that he had not seen for two months. In some the same serial was running, but he had lost interest in the best of them, since the thread had been broken.

"I should think a series of stories about the same character would bind a reader to a particular magazine," he mused aloud, "but each story should be complete in one issue. Then if the reader missed one month or six, it would make no difference."

"It certainly is disappointing to get well into a story then have to wait a month for the next episode—and perhaps miss it entirely!" Touie agreed.

No more had been said on the subject, but Arthur was busy. He opened his new offices on April 2, 1891, and the following day he mailed "A Scandal in Bohemia" to a literary agent, A. P. Watt. The agent submitted the story to Greenhough Smith, editor of a new magazine, the *Strand*.

"Please bring Dr. Conan Doyle around for tea at your earliest convenience," editor Smith wrote Mr. Watt.

Arthur liked the heavily mustached, bespectacled editor at once.

"Your plan for individual stories featuring the same characters is a good one," Smith told Conan Doyle and his agent. They were sipping their tea in the dingy offices on Burleigh Street in the Strand, a close-packed business section of London. "Our magazine caters to the new readers created as a result of the Public Education Act passed a few years ago. Holmes and Watson are perfectly suited to this popular taste. I believe our owner, George Newnes, would give you a contract for a series."

April sunlight filtered through the one grimy window to speckle the desk with gold. A stack of manuscripts teetered on one side; more were piled behind the editor's desk.

How many hopeful writers there are in the world, thought Conan Doyle. How did they ever happen to notice an obscure doctor at all!

"I would only wish to tie myself down to six stories just now," he said aloud. "I rather think the public will tire of these characters before those six are done. But if you wish to take the chance . . ."

They settled on thirty-five pounds per story less the agent's fee, and the contract was drawn up.

Had even a single patient entered Dr. Conan Doyle's consulting room during the month of April, 1891, he would have found the "eye specialist" diligently filling page after page of foolscap with his neat small script. On April 10, "A Case of Identity" went off to the *Strand*. "The Red-Headed League" followed on April 20, and on April 27, "The Boscombe Valley Mystery" joined the rest.

Arthur had just begun "The Adventure of the Five Orange Pips" when fate delayed its progress. He left his home early on the first of May to walk the few blocks to his office. He had gone only a short distance when he was taken with a chill and dizziness and collapsed. The sudden and violent onset of the fever convinced him that he had influenza.

In the weeks that his fever raged, he lay close to death's door. The fever left him weak physically, but during his convalescence he did a great deal of thinking about himself. For the first time in years, he saw his future clearly.

"How foolish to maintain an expensive oculist's rooms near fashionable Wimpole Street," he told himself, "on money earned through my writings!"

A sense of wild joy seized him. His fingers grasped a handkerchief lying on the coverlet. Feebly he tossed it into the air and cheered. The squeak that emerged from his throat brought Touie running. She had not been out of earshot for two weeks.

"What is it, Arthur?" she asked, alarmed.

"I shall cut the painter, my dear, and trust to my power of writing!" he announced. "No longer shall I conform to professional dress," he gloated, "nor try to please anyone else!"

9. The Doll and Its Maker

The first of the Sherlock Holmes adventures, "A Scandal in Bohemia," appeared in the July issue of *Strand Magazine*. Arthur and Touie were busy settling into their new home at 12 Tennison Road, South Norwood, a London suburb.

"The air comes straight from the hills of Surrey," he announced, pointing to the sweep of rolling green countryside beyond the garden. "Next year I shall lay out a tennis lawn. Right now I have a surprise for you, Touie."

He led her through the back gate. Against the wall stood a red tandem bicycle. "We can ride all over the countryside," he exulted. "The hills start only thirty miles north of here. Good sport, what?"

Touie's heart sank at the thought of pedaling such a distance. The efforts of the past year had severely taxed her strength—closing Southsea, the dash across Europe, then back, the months in lodgings again with a toddler who must be constantly watched. Finally, Arthur's illness had drained her last ounce of energy.

"I'll do all the pedaling, love," promised Arthur. Her husband's lusty enthusiasm was contagious. "I am a free man," he exclaimed over and over, expanding his enormous chest to inhale the sparkling air.

His study to the right of the front door was already cluttered with books and folders of notes on the history of France; his visit to that country had sparked a new historical novel. He envisioned a sweeping saga about the persecution of the Huguenots that would transport the reader from the glittering courts of the Sun King, Louis XIV, to the forbidding forests of Canada.

He was deep in the first chapters of *The Refugees* when the long fingers of Sherlock Holmes stayed his pen.

"The Holmes stories will be exhausted by the end of the year," wrote editor Greenhough Smith.

Sherlock Holmes' adventures had captured the public imagination. The developing personality of the great sleuth was perfectly illustrated by the accomplished artist Sidney Paget. "A Scandal in Bohemia" introduced a tall Holmes but not skinny. He had the high "frontal development" which Doyle insisted denoted uncommon cerebral development. His nose was long and well-shaped. Standing before the fireplace at Baker Street, pondering a case, or attending a concert, he was always correctly attired in striped trousers, vest and frock coat.

"The intellectual and the accomplished musician as well as the master sleuth," pointed out his creator. "I must say Paget's caught the many facets of Holmes' character very well."

When Holmes went to the country, as was necessary to solve "The Boscombe Valley Mystery," he appeared for the first time in country garb—the deerstalker hat and long gray traveling cloak.

In all the stories, Holmes showed a remarkable chameleon ability. On several occasions he fooled his dependable but credulous friend Watson with his disguises. In "Scandal," Holmes attired himself as a groom—"ill-kempt and side-whiskered, with an inflamed face and disreputable clothes"

—in order to get into a lady's house. In "The Man with the Twisted Lip," Watson literally stumbled over an ancient smoker in an opium den who revealed himself later as Holmes.

By October, Smith's pleas for more Holmes stories became frantic. He reminded Conan Doyle of all the ancient gentlemen in hundreds of clubs across the Empire who lived only for the next Holmes mystery. He told of thousands of public school boys who had discovered the sleuth during the long holiday and now risked any punishment to smuggle the latest issue of the *Strand* into their bleak dormitories. Most of all there were the ladies, whose lives were as barren of adventure as their parlors were cluttered.

". . . all sing a veritable hymn of praise to Mr. Sherlock Holmes!" wrote the editor. "We must have more."

Conan Doyle talked the matter over with his agent. "I am reluctant to leave *The Refugees* to do more Holmes stories," he confessed. "Each story needs as clear-cut and original a plot as would a longish book."

"They pay well for those tales," reminded Mr. Watt.

"Yes, but I am under no financial pressure just now," argued Conan Doyle. "If I must sustain this Holmes character longer, I wish the public to find the last story as good as the first."

"The *Strand* are simply imploring me to continue Holmes," he wrote his mother. "Perhaps I could ask a price so high they will abandon him. I will write by this post to say that if they offer me 50 pounds each, irrespective of *length,* I may be induced to consider my refusal. Seems rather high-handed, does it not?"

The *Strand* asked for more stories.

Autumn gales shook the little house in South Norwood as Conan Doyle toiled to spin his plots. Many of his ideas he found among the mounds of newspaper clippings that he had been collecting since the early days at Southsea—records of strange crimes, especially those that the police had been unable to solve. To them, he applied the special genius of Sherlock Holmes.

The first of the new series was a Christmas story, "The Adventure of the Blue Carbuncle." With the aid of a battered hat, Holmes deduced how the unusual gem, worth one thousand pounds, happened into the crop of a Christmas goose. Having trapped the would-be thief as well, he let him go.

"I am not retained by the police to supply their deficiencies," he explains to Dr. Watson. "I suppose that I am committing a felony, but it is just possible that I am saving a soul. Besides, it is the season of forgiveness . . ."

Thus Mr. Sherlock Holmes established himself as a "regular hero" with every Cockney, factory hand and farmer's son who could spell out the words of the stories.

Conan Doyle had established a routine of working from 8:00 A.M. until noon, then from 5:00 P.M. to dinnertime at 8:00. Afternoons he took his exercise. With Touie perched on the front saddle of the tandem, he roamed the countryside for miles, pumping vigorously up and down dale. The crisp air cleared his mind. Often he returned with his latest case solved. The work went swiftly.

"In the last week," he wrote the Ma'am at the end of October, "I have done two of the new Sherlock Holmes stories—'The Adventure of the Blue Carbuncle' and 'The Adventure of the Speckled Band.' The latter is a thriller. I see my way through the ninth, so that I should not have much trouble with the rest. . . . The twelve should make a nice little book. I think of slaying Holmes in the last and winding him up for good. He takes my mind from other things."

"You wouldn't dare!" was the Ma'am's shocked reply. She

was an ardent fan of Sherlock. Arthur sent all the proof sheets to her for criticism and suggestions.

That winter, Jerome K. Jerome, editor of a new magazine, *The Idler,* introduced Conan Doyle to literary London. He published several of Conan Doyle's medical stories—and made him a member of the "Idler's" club.

At club dinners, Conan Doyle met many writers, among them gruffly affable Rudyard Kipling, whose writings had delighted him ever since he had spent his last shilling for a copy of *Plain Tales.* There was sardonic, red-bearded Bernard Shaw, who always took the opposite side of any argument no matter what he really believed, just for the sake of argument. There was the little Scotchman, James Barrie, as merry as Shaw was sour, and a fellow alumnus from Edinburgh University.

Friendships flourished in the mellow atmosphere where wine and jokes flowed freely. The rugged doctor with his round, ruddy face and curling mustache was a popular addition to the group. His hearty laugh echoed down the long table. Even the most reserved asked: "Who is that jolly fellow?"

Inevitably some wit replied: "Why, Dr. Watson, I presume." Dr. Conan Doyle might be a newcomer, but Holmes and Watson were old friends to most of the members.

James Barrie was quick to see the annoyance on Arthur's face.

"It's all very well to be mistaken for one of your own characters," piped the gnomelike Scot, his domed forehead creased with laughter. "Sure back in Kirriemuir, they're disbelievin' that I could gain a reputation in London at all!" The author of the popular *Window in Thrums* chuckled delightedly. "Some think my excellent handwriting must have caused my success. Others believe I print my books myself and hawk them about on the streets."

After dinner, Conan Doyle thanked Barrie for intervening. "I consider Holmes and Watson among my lesser creations," he explained, "so I become unreasonably angry when reminded of the stature they have attained in the public mind. Would you believe those characters receive mail! Pleas to solve some local or family mystery—that sort of thing. One came from Poland the other day asking Holmes to travel there, all expenses paid. Press cutting services keep soliciting Watson's business. Really, the thing's gone too far!"

Barrie's first play, *Walker, London,* renewed Conan Doyle's love of the theater, and he decided to try to adapt one of his own short stories for the stage. Ever since he had seen Henry Irving in *Hamlet,* he had followed the great actor's career. Now he sought a character suited to his boyhood idol's talents. He found him in Corporal Gregory Brewster, aged veteran of the Battle of Waterloo.

"The Straggler of '15" was the story of a ninety-year-old corporal dying in a tiny room, all but forgotten. The unexpected entry of a uniformed man kindles the memory of heroic moments lived many years before. The one-act play, which Conan Doyle called *Waterloo,* would depend entirely on the performance of the actor who played Corporal Gregory Brewster. It was a perfect vehicle for a superb actor. Henry Irving bought the copyright as soon as it was offered him.

The prospect of having Irving bring to life one of his brainchildren was not the only triumph of that winter. *The White Company,* just published in book form, was receiving excellent reviews. Only Conan Doyle was not pleased. He stalked into the drawing room one evening shaking a batch of the first reviews at a startled Touie and his sister Connie, who had left her governess post to live with them.

"They praise *The White Company* as a roaring adventure story!" Arthur cried, his face red with rage. "They do not

even mention that it is also an exact picture of the life and
times of the bowman soldier, one of the most important figures in British military history. You know the research I
did, Touie."

"Yes, dear, but when you put it in a story, it doesn't
show," his wife reminded him. "You write with such ease!"

Most exasperating to Arthur were the continuing letters
from Greenhough Smith urging him to do more Sherlock
Holmes stories. Anxious to finish *The Refugees,* he tried to
ignore them.

"I am done with Holmes," he said over and over.

The public thought otherwise. Interviewers who flocked to
Tennison Road were surprised by the tall, soldierly figure
they found chipping away at golf balls in the back yard.
Surely, they thought, the rough country tweeds, the ruddy
mustached face, belonged to Watson not Holmes. The study
to which Conan Doyle led them was as comfortably cluttered as the one described at 221b Baker Street. But behind
their host's candid blue eyes there could not exist the "cal-
culating machine" that deduced a man's innermost secrets
from the cut of his vest. Who then was Sherlock Holmes?
they asked.

"The famous Edinburgh surgeon, Dr. Joseph Bell, was
my model," Conan Doyle told them.

When newshawks searched out the lanky hawk-faced Dr.
Bell, he looked enough like an aging Sherlock to please them.

"By his imaginative genius, Dr. Conan Doyle has made
a great deal out of very little," the surgeon told reporters.
"Holmes' methods of deduction have certainly been used by
me in diagnosis. But I have never been able to offer Dr.
Doyle one single workable plot, and," the doctor confessed
ruefully, "it's not for want of trying."

Fellow authors appreciated the craftsmanship that had
created such lifelike characters as Sherlock Holmes and Dr.

Watson. From faraway Samoa, where issues of *Strand Magazine* with the first Holmes stories were just arriving, came a letter from another Edinburgh alumnus whom Arthur had always admired but never met.

"Surely this is my old friend Joe Bell!" wrote Robert Louis Stevenson. "I have been telling the yarn of 'The Engineer's Thumb' to my native servants. It is difficult to explain to them what a railway is and an engineer. They remain convinced that you actually experienced the weird adventure. If you could have seen the bright feverish eyes of Simite you would have tasted glory!"

"Yet I am beginning to wonder myself if I have the qualities of mind of Sherlock Holmes," Conan Doyle confessed to James Barrie. The two were walking on the moor near Barrie's home just north of the English border. The highlands were turning from winter gray to the heather purple of spring.

"You have more human qualities than you attribute to your Sherlock," Barrie mused. "Yet you could not spin so lifelike a character unless you had within you some possibilities of that character."

"Well, that would be a dangerous admission for one who has drawn as many villains as I." Conan Doyle laughed. "No. Only the other day I wrote this bit of doggerel to a critic who had attributed to me some opinions expressed by Holmes: 'Please grip this fact with your cerebral tentacle,/ The doll and its maker are never identical.' "

"You've missed your calling," laughed Barrie. "You could make more money writing lyrics for light opera a la Gilbert and Sullivan! Seriously though, you should insert clues into your stories to show that you are Sherlock Holmes. Otherwise future scholars will argue endlessly as to who he was and who wrote the stories."

"Oh, the clues are there, if anyone is sharp enough to spot

them. But there'll be no more mysteries now. I instructed my agent to tell the *Strand* I want a thousand pounds a story. Presumptuous, what?"

Arthur returned to South Norwood eager to complete *The Great Shadow,* a novel about Napoleon and his conquest of Europe. On his desk was a letter from Greenhough Smith. When could he schedule the next series of Sherlock Holmes tales?

The request astonished Doyle. *Micah Clarke* and *The White Company* were selling into edition after edition; he had expected they would. The Sherlock Holmes stories had been translated into French, and his publisher planned to make them into a book titled *The Adventures of Sherlock Holmes;* this too he had foreseen.

Even the fact that both Scotland Yard and the French Sûreté were adopting some of Sherlock Holmes' methods of crime detection—such as casting footsteps in plaster and analyzing bloodstains, dust, cigar ash and the like—was not surprising. With advances in science, such innovations would have come in due course. He was deeply gratified when the police at Lyons, France, named their new laboratories in his honor.

But one thousand pounds a story was a small fortune! Still, he must ask the *Strand* to wait until he had completed *The Great Shadow* for Arrowsmith publishers.

"I'm becoming a celebrity!" he exclaimed aloud.

"Of course, my dear," replied Touie quietly.

10. *The Reichenbach Fall*

Touie could not longer go spinning across country on the front seat of the tandem; she was expecting another baby in the autumn. So Arthur turned to another sport—lawn tennis. He was never without a match, for family and friends flocked round the new attraction.

His brother, Innes, now a tall nineteen and preparing for a military career at nearby Woolwich, was a frequent visitor. A vigorous player, he gave his elder brother a hard game. When finally worn out, they donned corduroy jackets and straw boaters to lounge with Touie and sip cold tea while watching the others play. Beautiful Connie, playing with a succession of admirers, poked delicately at the ball. A dapper white-flanneled journalist, Ernest William Hornung, nosed out her other suitors and a wedding was in the offing. Arthur and Touie were trying to like the sharp-tongued dandy, whose puns set their teeth on edge.

"Though he might be more humble, there is no police like Holmes," was one of "Willie's" favorite quips.

At midsummer, Conan Doyle was working on the new Sherlock Holmes series. He had completed *The Great Shadow*, with the help of Connie, who had learned to use the typewriter. Arthur considered this novel about Napo-

leon his finest historical work. He whisked Touie off to Norway for a quiet holiday and returned with three mysteries
completed. The first, a story of horses and horse racing titled
"Silver Blaze," was a favorite.

"Holmes is in top form," he wrote his agent, "though my
ignorance of horses and racing may cry aloud to heaven!"

He had barely begun work on the fourth story, the case
of "The Stock-Broker's Clerk," when he received an urgent telegram from James Barrie.

"Could you possibly help me out with the librettos of a
light opera?"

Arthur found Barrie run-down and nervous. He had
promised to write an opera for D'Oyly Carte in the great
Gilbert and Sullivan tradition. The first act was done and
the second roughed out.

"What is it about?" asked Conan Doyle taking off his
coat. He knew little about light opera, nothing at all about
music. But his friend needed help, and he believed that a
writer worth his salt should be able to tackle anything from
a scientific treatise to a comic song.

"The scene is a girls' school," Barrie explained. "The two
heroes, an officer in the Lancers and an Oxford undergraduate, get into the bedroom floor of the seminary—"

"Good Heavens! You can't hope to get away with that."

"Oh, it's all very innocent." Barrie chuckled. "The Proctor
pursues the undergraduate. He hides in the grandfather
clock and sings a duet with the schoolmarm."

Amid uproarious laughter the two authors pounded out
Jane Annie, or The Good-Conduct Prize.

"I don't know when I have had such good fun," admitted
Conan Doyle as the two strode along the beach chewing on
their unlit clay pipes.

"Your very presence has cured me," Barrie told him. "Can

I help now with Holmes? I'm no good at sleuthing, but a plot perhaps?"

"How can I kill him?"

"Oh, come now, Doyle! Aren't you being ungrateful? Holmes has been a friend to you in many ways."

"If I tend to tire of him," Arthur explained, "it is because his character admits of no light or shade. The variety of the stories depends entirely on the plots. Sooner or later I'm bound to run out of ideas, so I must get rid of poor old Sherlock Holmes."

Lottie returned from Portugal in October, just in time to greet the arrival of her nephew, in November, 1892.

Always "My son" to Arthur, the choosing of his name was an agonizing family decision. In the handsome drawing room with its design of cabbage roses in the carpet, the silk-shaded gas lamps, and vases of pampas grass on the marble fireplace, they read over and over the list sent by the Ma'am "in the wonderful event of a boy."

"Kingsley appeals to me as much as any," decided Mrs. Hawkins.

"It's a lovely name," the girls agreed.

In the end, Arthur settled on Alleyne Kingsley, in honor of Squire Alleyne Edricson, hero of *The White Company*.

By the time Christmas arrived, he had finished the last of eight more Holmes stories for the new series, scheduled to start early in 1893.

"I feel like a man who has consumed too much pâté de foie gras," he told his family at Christmas dinner. "The very mention of Sherlock Holmes nauseates me!"

The Ma'am, with Ida and Claire, whom the family still called "Dodo," had come down from Yorkshire for a few days. Mrs. Doyle seldom visited, for every day she drove her dogcart across the gusty moor to visit her husband in the nursing home.

"But your father seldom knows me now," she told Arthur.

Conan Doyle dressed as Father Christmas for the yearly party to which all the neighborhood children were invited. Big and hearty, he appeared a real, though giant-size, edition of the jolly elf. Touie laughed so much that she started a coughing fit, and Lottie had to help her to her room.

"I'm going to take Touie to Switzerland next month," Arthur told his sister that evening. "She has not gotten her strength back since the baby arrived. And I don't like that cough. The damp English winter is no good for her."

In the high clear air of Interlaken, with the green promise of spring below and the white-crowned peaks above, Touie's cheeks grew pink and her energy returned. Arthur felt his own exhaustion ebb away, though he still had no desire to set pen to paper. For once he was satisfied with Touie's short walks, a game of bowls while she rested, and a dance or rubber of whist before bedtime.

"It's like a honeymoon." Touie basked in her husband's full attention for the first time since their marriage.

When both were rested, they took a trip to view the famous Reichenbach Fall. Their first sight of the fall was a shaft of green-blue water that seemed to shoot off into the air then plunge into a chasm of glistening black rock. Arthur stepped up to the guardrail and found himself staring into a boiling caldron of immeasurable depth. Fine spray hissed upward from the white foam where the narrowing chasm pushed the roaring water back against itself, before it escaped over the jagged lip of rock to the valley far below. Instinctively Arthur put a protective arm around Touie when he heard her gasp of awe. It was indeed a fearful place, enough to turn a strong man giddy with its constant whirl and clamor.

"The sound is almost like the cry of a human in dire distress," exclaimed Touie, backing away.

Conan Doyle stood listening to that half-human shout with secret exultation. Here was the perfect spot to dispose of Sherlock Holmes without a trace.

Jane Annie opened at the Savoy in July, 1893. It was a flop. That summer, Connie married her Willie in a small garden ceremony. In October Charles Doyle died. Arthur had never been close to the strange withdrawn man who was his father, but he admired the genius which produced the paintings on his study wall.

"Someday I shall make a collection of all his works and exhibit them in London," Arthur wrote. But that day would have to wait.

Touie had been complaining of a pain in her side, and her cough had become more persistent. Arthur still suspected nothing serious, but called in a neighboring physician, Dr. Dalton, to examine her. The doctor was grave when he came down from her bedroom.

"Your wife has every sign of a rapid type of consumption," was his diagnosis. "Her lungs appear to be seriously affected already. I wish you would have a second opinion, of course," he added cautiously.

Sir Douglas Powell, a specialist in lung diseases, confirmed his opinion, and told Arthur, "I'm afraid she has not many months to live."

The world that Conan Doyle had built so laboriously suddenly crashed around him. All the years of struggle and sacrifice to become a doctor, the hours of research and writing, first to keep body and soul together, then to make a home for his wife and family. What was the good of it all now?

He remembered the sound of endless scales as Touie patiently instructed her pupils in the rudiments of music to make a few extra shillings. He remembered how tired she became on the long walks and cycle rides he enjoyed.

"You must not blame yourself," Lottie comforted him. "Touie's pleasure is doing what you like to do. And she enjoyed her little pupils at Southsea. But she has always been fragile."

"And I have been selfish and blind!" Arthur cried out in his grief. "The thought of life without Touie's sunny presence—no it is unthinkable! I shall not give up without a fight."

He told Touie, "We will go to Davos in the High Alps." It is in eastern Switzerland near the Austrian border, close to where I went to school. That climate will surely make you better. Lottie and children will go with us."

"But our home, Arthur?"

"Your mother wishes to stay and keep the house," he assured her.

In the high sunlit valley, sheltered from all wind, Touie improved so much that Arthur began to feel he could will her wasting disease away. He settled down to write again, a fictionalized biography titled *The Stark Munro Letters.*

Using the device of a young doctor's letters to a friend in America, Conan Doyle attempted "to give a faithful rendering of a modern young man with his relations to life." A sense of futility and gloom permeated the book. Yet his irrepressible humor broke through like sunshine on a cloudy day, especially in the account of his association with Dr. Budd, whom he called Cullingworth.

While Conan Doyle was fighting his own tragic battle, his readers were plunged into grief by the publication of Sherlock Holmes' *Final Problem,* in December, 1893.

It is with heavy heart (wrote Dr. Watson) that I take up my pen to write these the last words in which I shall ever

record the singular gift by which my friend Mr. Sherlock
Holmes was distinguished.

In attempting to track down the master criminal, Professor Moriarty, Holmes himself became the quarry. The chase
took them half across Europe until they met on the slippery
path beside the Reichenbach Fall.

An examination by experts leaves little doubt that a personal contest between the two men ended, as it could hardly
fail to end, in their reeling over, locked in each other's arms.
Any attempt at recovering the bodies was absolutely hope-
less, and there, deep down in that dreadful cauldron of
swirling water and seething foam, will lie for all time the
most dangerous criminal and the foremost champion of the
law. . . .

Conan Doyle's public was shocked and furious. Letters
poured in so abusive that his publisher and agent hesitated
to forward them. He was denounced as a murderer and
worse. One woman addressed him simply as "You brute!"

"Sporting young city men are appearing at their offices
with black crepe bands tied round their hats in mourning
for Sherlock Holmes!" wrote A. P. Watt, Doyle's agent.

In the sunlit veranda of the Kurhaus Hotel, it all seemed
very far away. Arthur looked at his wife's sweet face, so thin
yet always cheerful, and wondered how people could get so
excited about a fictional character. He told her nothing
about the death of Holmes or its aftermath. Lottie kept
issues of the *Strand* hidden from Touie.

"She'll think you killed him off because of her," Lottie
told her brother one evening after tucking Touie and the
children off to bed.

"But that series was written long before we knew of her illness."

"I know, but it's as if you had foresight," his sister mused. "I mean, Sherlock Holmes is left alone beside the fall only when Dr. Watson is called away to care for a lady from Davos who is dying of consumption."

11. Sportsman and Traveler

In the hotel's small library, Conan Doyle discovered the *Memoirs of General de Marbot*. As a captain in Napoleon's Grand Army, De Marbot had marched and fought his way across Europe. He described his exploits and adventures in lyric French and with a typical Gallic pride that delighted Arthur. The dashing officer, whose conceit was excelled only by his courage, sprang fully armed from the pages of his memoirs. For the first time since Arthur learned of Touie's illness, the cloud of depression that had engulfed him lifted.

"A swashbuckling French hero would make the public forget Sherlock Holmes!" he exclaimed aloud. With a surge of joy that came with a new and exciting idea, he began to write about a new hero, twenty-year-old Brigadier Étienne Gerard of the Emperor's Hussars.

When Arthur was not working, he was tumbling about in the snow with his five-year-old daughter Mary, or walking about the sunbright valley. The upper mountain slopes and passes were deep in drifts. There was no way to reach the next valley except by a roundabout railway journey.

"I have been reading how the Norwegian explorer Fridtjof Nansen crossed Greenland on skis," Conan Doyle told

Tobias Branger, a tradesman in sporting goods in Davos. "I believe one could cross over the high passes to neighboring valleys in the same manner."

Branger interested his brother in the idea, and they agreed to import skis from Norway and try it out.

"You cannot appreciate this yet," the English author assured guests at the hotel, "but the time will come when hundreds of Englishmen will come to Switzerland for a skiing season."

By autumn, 1894, Touie was so much improved that Arthur felt safe in leaving her to make a long deferred lecture tour in the United States.

"Only be back for Christmas," Touie urged.

Innes had graduated that spring from Woolwich. Now twenty-one and a subaltern in the Royal Artillery, he jumped at the opportunity to accompany his brother to America.

The brothers sailed on the German liner *Elbe,* arriving in New York early in October. They were met by Major Pond, a huge loose-limbed Civil War veteran with a goatee. A genial host, he had arranged a schedule that would have intimidated a lesser man than Conan Doyle. Arthur was booked for a series of "Readings and Reminiscences" in every major town between Boston and Washington to the south, Chicago and Milwaukee to the west.

"Sherlock Holmes is very popular here in the states," Pond repeated often in his nasal voice, "very popular indeed, Dr. Watson—er—uh—I mean Dr. Doyle."

Arthur had always thought London noisy and dirty, but he found New York appalling. Electric cable cars whizzed along the avenue called Broadway with such a clamor that he wondered why the cab horses did not bolt. To add to the confusion, trains ran overhead making some of the avenues quite dark at midday.

Their host did not immediately notice the visitors' discomfort as he pointed with pride to a phenomenon he called the "skyscraper."

"This is Number One Broadway," he told the Doyles, "the Washington Building built in 1882 and for several years the tallest building in the world. Now the Manhattan Life Insurance Company has erected one taller—here, Number Sixty-six Broadway. Its tower is higher than the cross on old Trinity Church. Joe Pulitzer of *The New York World* put up another skyscraper with a dome on it near City Hall."

"I can see that New Yorkers must get up in the sky to get away from their filthy streets," remarked Arthur with customary candor. Every side street was lined with overflowing trash cans, and gutters were choked with refuse. A miasma hung over the city.

"Politics!" exclaimed Pond in disgust. "But we've finally got Tammany out of City Hall. The new mayor, William Strong, inherited a fearful mess that will take some time to clean up. Driver"—Pond leaned forward—"go over to the East River and show our English visitors the Brooklyn Bridge. That miracle of engineering should divert you from the stench of our politics," he told the brothers.

A nervous Conan Doyle made his first American appearance at the Calvary Baptist Church on West 57th Street. On the very edge of the platform, he had discovered his collar stud was gone. Only the loan of Major Pond's had enabled him to pull his collar together and redo his tie. The incident added to his unsettled feeling, but once on his feet, all nervousness left him.

"The moment the man spoke," reported *The New York World*, "Sherlock Holmes would have said he was a 'good fellow'; a generous man, for he spoke in a melodious, hearty, welcoming voice. . . . He used none of the tricks of elocutionists, very few gestures or stagy tricks. . . ."

He read excerpts from his historical works and the new

Brigadier Gerard series as well as from the Sherlock Holmes stories. He talked a little of how he came to write each book, how he did his research, how he felt about his characters.

But everywhere he met skepticism when he referred to Sherlock Holmes and Dr. Watson as fictional characters.

"They want to believe those two are real people!" he finally concluded, "or rather were, since Holmes, at least, is supposed to be dead. Many won't even accept that. They think that I am Watson and am hiding him somewhere so Moriarty's gang can't get him!"

"You'd do well to foster the illusion, I should think," Innes told him.

For the most part, Conan Doyle's meeting with America and Americans was a love affair from the start.

"I have found all the good I expected," Arthur wrote his mother. "The women are not as attractive as we had been told. The children are bright and pretty, though there is a tendency to spoil them. The race as a whole is not only the most prosperous, but the most even-tempered, tolerant, and hopeful that I have ever known. They meet their own problems in their own way, and precious little sympathy they ever get from England."

The anti-British feeling he sensed everywhere in the Midwest disturbed him. At a banquet in Detroit where the wine flowed freely, one of the hosts ended the evening by denouncing the British Empire so loudly that Conan Doyle was moved to reply. Club members later assured him they would never forget his words.

"You Americans have lived up to now within your own palings," he informed them, "and know nothing of the world outside. But now your land is filled up, and you will be compelled to mix more with the other nations. When you do so you will find that there is only one which can at all understand your ways and your aspirations, or will have the least sympathy. That is the mother country which you are now so fond of insulting. She is an Empire, and you will soon be an Empire also, and only then will you understand each other, and you will realize that you have only one real friend in the world."

In making the American tour at this time, Conan Doyle was forced to miss the opening of his first play, *Waterloo*. Echoes of the applause that greeted Henry Irving's magnificent portrayal of Corporal Gregory Brewster pulsed across the Atlantic cable from Bristol, England, all the way to Chicago.

Back in New York, the size of his audiences doubled. From there, they journeyed through New England. They made a pilgrimage to Mount Auburn Cemetery to pay homage to Oliver Wendell Holmes, Henry Wadsworth Longfellow, James Russell Lowell and the many other literary greats buried there. Arthur laid a wreath on Holmes' grave, lingering there a long time as once he had beside Macaulay's tomb.

"How can one love so much a man one has never seen?" he wondered aloud. "I would like to believe, as some do, that I may someday converse with great spirits that have passed on."

At Brattleboro, Vermont, Arthur visited two days with his old friend Rudyard Kipling and his American bride, Caroline Starr Balestier. The Kiplings' home, shaped like Noah's Ark, was a haven after the succession of hotel rooms and banquets. The wiry little Englishman, his odd house and passion for privacy kept curiosity-seekers at a distance.

Conan Doyle persuaded Kipling to try out the golf clubs he had carried everywhere in hopes of finding a links.

"The game is as new in Europe as here," Arthur explained. "When my clubs went astray on a German railway last summer, they turned up with an official tag describing them as *Kinderspieler,* child's toys!"

"I have never been any good at sports," said Kipling. "But there's plenty of room in the fields around town. You can give me a lesson."

The citizens of Brattleboro were amazed to see grown men indulging in such a strange pastime. Before they had practiced five minutes, the whole town was out to see the big English doctor with his funny cap trying to hit a tiny white ball with a long stick.

By the time the Doyle brothers sailed on December 7, Arthur had received more honors from clubs and societies than any other Englishman. He had given forty readings and made a thousand pounds over expenses.

"I can promise much more than that if you'll return for a hundred nights!" vowed Major Pond.

On board ship, Arthur sank into his bed exhausted and remained there till he reached Liverpool. He was back with Touie for Christmas.

In Davos, the winter season was in full swing. The Branger brothers had received the skis from Norway, and for some weeks the three tumbled about the slopes near the hotel to the vast entertainment of guests and villagers.

After a month or so, they decided they were expert enough to climb the Jacobshorn, a considerable hill opposite the hotel. They had to carry the unwieldy skis past the fir trees to the deep snow of the open slope. Then on skis, they shuffled laboriously up the steep incline by long zigzags. When they finally reached the top, they had the satisfaction of seeing the flags in the village dipped in honor of their accomplishment.

Then came the reward. Turning their skis downward, they glided delightfully over the gentle slopes, fairly flew down the steep ones.

"We took an occasional cropper," Arthur admitted to his family excitedly that evening. "But the feeling is as near to flying as earthbound man can get. With the keen air blowing against your cheeks, it's a glorious experience!"

Conan Doyle was determined to prove that skiing was a useful accomplishment by crossing over the high pass to the neighboring valley of Arosa. The setting moon still shone on unbroken snow as the men made their way one icy morning toward the pass, thousands of feet higher than the peak of the Jacobshorn. They had no rope, and Arthur dared not look at some of the chasms they passed. From the corner of his eye he could see blue vapor rising from the abyss.

By the time they reached the pass, the sun was high but had not yet softened the snow in some places. It was necessary to stamp with their skis in order to get any foothold. The Brangers clomped along on either side of Conan Doyle so that if he slipped they would bear the brunt of his weight. They had dropped about halfway down toward Arosa, and Arthur was already feeling the exhilarated pride of the pioneer, when they came to a slope that appeared almost perpendicular. The three stared dumbfounded.

"I suppose the Norwegians would know how to maneuver that precipice," observed Conan Doyle.

However, his companions apparently had picked up a few tricks themselves. They unstrapped their skis, then lashed them together to make a toboggan, and pushing themselves over the edge, flew down in a cloud of snow. As Conan Doyle prepared to follow, his skis shot out from under him and down the slope. The shocked Brangers stood helplessly watching the skis fly toward them.

Arthur gritted his teeth and did the one thing left to him. Squatting down, he extended his legs and arms to check his momentum and let himself go over the edge. A moment later he was rolling over at the feet of his guides, drenched in

snow, but unhurt. The skis were safe in a mound of snow
nearby, and the three continued their victorious *"schuss"* to
Arosa. When they returned to the hotel Tobias Branger
entered his name in the register—"Dr. Doyle, Sportsman."

The rains came early that spring, putting an end to skiing. Conan Doyle restlessly paced the big veranda of the
Kurhaus and talked to the innkeeper about golf.

"It is the most maddening game I have ever played, and I
have tried most. I never hope to be any good at it. But there's
no doubt it will become a fad. You must have a links."

So he and a few enthusiastic guests sloshed across the
muddy meadows around the hotel to lay out a crude golf
course. The work was hampered by the cows who chewed up
the red flags marking the holes.

Toward summer, the Doyles moved on to Caux, at the
top of Lake Geneva, where Arthur completed a novel about
boxing called *Rodney Stone*. He was a keen boxer himself.
His ability had come in handy aboard the whaler more than
once. During his travels around Sussex as a medical student,
he had insured his popularity among the young farmers by
putting on the gloves and going a few rounds for the fun
of it. But on the whole, boxing was no longer as popular in
England as it had once been.

"Why boxing?" asked Sir George Newnes, owner of *Strand
Magazine,* when Conan Doyle gave him the manuscript.

"I am of the opinion that the prize ring was an excellent
thing from a national point of view," Arthur explained.
"Better that our sports should be a little too rough than that
we should run the risk of effeminacy. Boxing was once a
favored sport of princes and kings, and my book may make it
so again."

Reluctantly Newnes and his editor, Greenhough Smith,
consented to publish the novel. Then Arthur rushed down to
South Norwood to see his mother-in-law.

Mrs. Hawkins was a forlorn figure waiting on the steps of the empty house on Tennison Street. She appeared to have shrunk several inches, and her hair was snow white.

"I am putting this house on the market," Arthur told her, "and building a home at Hindhead in Surrey where we can all be together again!"

"But Touie?"

"The wretched microbe that has disrupted all our lives appears to be latent," he assured her. "At lunch the other day a friend who suffers from consumption told me that he has found his salvation in the dry air of Surrey. I lost no time in buying land there, and my old friend from Southsea, Mr. Ball, has already drawn up plans and engaged a builder."

Tears of joy ran down Mrs. Hawkins wrinkled cheeks. She knew all too well the frustration of traveling from resort to resort in search of health. Arthur patted her thin shoulders fondly.

"One winter in Egypt should end our exile and your loneliness," he promised.

12. ◆ *Reporter in the Desert*

Conan Doyle's fame had preceded him to Cairo. Sherlock Holmes had been translated into the Egyptian language, and his adventures were being used by the local police as textbooks on modern methods of crime detection. The British were "temporarily" occupying Egypt in order to protect the Suez Canal, built at great expense and opened in 1869.

Seven miles out in the desert, in the shadow of the Pyramids, was the Mena Hotel where the Doyles made their headquarters. Touie blossomed in the dry heat, but Arthur found the climate so enervating that, for once, he could not even write.

He climbed the Great Pyramid once and found it "a futile and uncomfortable endeavor." Dubbing around the rudimentary golf links in front of the hotel was not much better. "It's a weird course," he told Touie and Lottie, "more sand-trap than fairway. And if you slice the ball, you're apt to find it bunkered in the grave of some Pharaoh!"

He tried horseback riding, was thrown and kicked above the right eye. An army surgeon vacationing at the hotel had to take five stitches in the star-shaped wound. Some nerves were damaged, for Conan Doyle was left with a drooping eyelid.

By the New Year, Touie was well enough to take one of Cook's boat trips up the Nile to Wadi Halfa, the last British outpost on the edge of the Nubian Desert. The majestic Nile, ribbon of life in the desert, cast its spell over them. But as the stern wheeler plowed towards the First Cataract at Assouan, Arthur began to realize they were in a danger-filled area. The Sudan was in revolt against the Khedive's government at Cairo. Fanatic followers of Mohammed Ahmed—"El Mahdi," hailed as the Messiah—swept noiselessly across the desert on fast loping camels to plunder mud villages along the Nile.

"The desert is like the sea. The camels are the ships," one of the tour directors explained. "On camelback, the Dervishes can attack without warning and disappear without a trace."

What's to prevent them from carrying off a Cook's excursion party? Arthur wondered.

They were standing on a rock at Abousir with a group of helpless tourists, mostly women, and only four soldiers for protection. Arthur found himself looking about anxiously. The heat pressed down like a blanket. Behind them, the desert stretched away to the horizon, silent yet ominous. In front, the broad river separated the party from the nearest English or Egyptian troops.

"We are safe on the water," the Egyptian guide was saying.

But we are not upon the water, thought Conan Doyle. Mahdi tribesmen might lurk behind every sand dune. In imagination he could almost hear the bloodthirsty scream of the Dervishes.

The rest of the trip passed swiftly as Conan Doyle began to spin one of his most suspenseful tales, which he called *A Tragedy of the Korosko.*

That spring of 1896, Major-General Horatio Kitchener,

commander of the British forces in Egypt, launched a campaign to pacify the Sudan. The grim, silent soldier, the scar of a Dervish bullet creasing his hawklike face, had grown impatient with Mahdi raids. Suddenly Egypt was the storm center of the world.

Conan Doyle could not sit idly while history was being made around him. All the big newspapers had correspondents in Africa, so he cabled *The Westminster Gazette,* requesting that they make him honorary correspondent, *pro tem.* Within a few days his papers arrived.

Arthur gathered his kit and made his way by river boat to Assouan, the same trip he had taken with Touie only a few months earlier.

The town and surrounding desert were alive with British troops waiting to be moved around the First Cataract. A narrow-gauge railroad carried all baggage and equipment thirty miles to Shellal, where it was reloaded on steamers. Chain gangs of convicts and fatigue parties of Egyptians labored night and day to speed the huge task, but all units were held up at least a week in the process.

Weary of waiting for action, Conan Doyle and four other newsmen, determined to move to the front on their own, bought camels and joined a cavalry force going south. After one day's ride in a cloud of sandy dust, they decided to go on alone rather than choke to death. It was a five-day journey across the desert to Korosko.

> I shall never forget those days [wrote Conan Doyle] or rather those nights, for we rose at two in the morning and our longest march was before or during the dawn. I am still haunted by that purple velvet sky, by those enormous and innumerable stars, by the half-moon which moved slowly above us, while our camels with their noiseless tread seemed to bear us without effort through a wonderful dream world.

For four days, the newsmen encountered only the creatures of the desert. Huge lizards sunned themselves along the banks of the Nile. One night Arthur saw a sluglike animal with horned projections on its head.

"That was an adder," one of his companions told him, "of the sort that sent Cleopatra to her death."

They had been sleeping in their blankets beneath the stars, but the following night they found a deserted hut in which to shelter. The light of their candle startled a creature Arthur thought was a mouse. It ran round and round, then up the wall and down again, until it came to rest, waving its forelegs at them. Suddenly one of the newsmen, a veteran of the desert, sprang into the air and came down on the animal with both feet, squashing it.

"Now why did you do that?" protested Doyle.

"That, dear fellow, was a tarantula!"

On the last morning of their journey, the men lingered after dawn in their grove of palm trees beside the path. Half-asleep, Arthur was startled by the sudden appearance of a horseman, a huge, fierce-looking Nubian covered with silver ornaments. A long rifle was slung across the warrior's back, and a sword dangled at his side. The barbaric figure answered the description of the Mahdi raiders against whom the correspondents had been warned.

Quietly Arthur reached over and touched his neighbor. The man's eyes opened, but the pressure on his arm kept him from making any other move.

"My God," Arthur heard him breathe when he saw the rider. Lying tense, they watched the sinister figure out of sight.

"Probably one of our own native tribesmen," they assured each other later. Nevertheless, they were glad to reach Korosko and board a steamer again.

From Wadi Halfa they pushed on to Sarras, where Kitchener had his advance headquarters. Sandbags and barbed wire surrounded the place attesting to the nearness of the enemy.

"El Mahdi will never make an open attack," Kitchener told the reporters whom he entertained at dinner one evening. "There will be no real action until I make it, and I must collect thousands more camels before I can advance."

April was far gone and the heat was already intense. Arthur knew he must return to take Touie north. He donated his camel to Kitchener's collection, then took the first boat back to Cairo.

By May 1, Conan Doyle was attending a Royal Academy banquet in London. Lights from the cut-glass chandeliers twinkled on the polished mahogany of the long table. The searing desert with its wild tribesmen seemed an incredible dream. But beneath the cuffs of his dress shirt, Arthur could feel the ragged ulcers on his wrists made by jiggers that had burrowed beneath his skin as he lay on the banks of the Nile.

13. ◆ *Army Surgeon*

Mary and Kingsley raced across the rolling heath of Hindhead. After the confinement of hotel life, the freedom of the fields was heaven. Behind them strode their father, breathing deep of the cool Surrey air. Together they were discovering wonders of which the children had never dreamed, and which Arthur had almost forgotten.

The wonder of all to seven-year-old Mary and her three-year-old brother was their father. The big stranger with the fierce mustaches was again the playful Daddy they remembered in Switzerland and Norwood. He did not seem awesome kneeling in the forest to point out a jack-in-the-pulpit or carrying a lost lamb back to its mother on his shoulder.

In the summer of 1897, the year of Queen Victoria's Diamond Jubilee, the Doyles moved into "Undershaw," named for the grove of larch trees that overhung Arthur's study. The mansion stood on a hill in the midst of four acres. At night it was brilliant with electric lamps, the current supplied by a private power plant. No other house in the neighborhood could boast such a luxury.

Below the hill was a tennis court. A billiard room stretched the length of one wing and contained the finest game equipment. In a sunny window overlooking the gardens stood a grand piano for Touie.

"You've waited a long time for a piano of your own," her husband reminded her.

"You didn't need to get a concert grand, Arthur! The best money can buy!" Her weakened fingers could only manage the lightest of tunes, and those very seldom.

Arthur kissed Touie's pale forehead. His hand rested momentarily on her soft brown hair, now streaked with gray, although she was only thirty-eight. She never complained of her restricted life. Only the inconvenience she caused others seemed to trouble her.

Conan Doyle settled into his regular writing routine. He completed his desert novel, *A Tragedy of the Korosko,* in which he captured perfectly the atmosphere of the upper Nile—the heat, the buzzing flies, the brooding desert with its gun-black rocks. His tourist party represented many nationalities and religious faiths. Their reaction to capture by the Mahdi, the behavior of each in the face of torture and the prospect of death, was a study in human nature.

"A rattling good adventure story," Arthur tagged it, but he hoped readers would find more in it. Like the tragedies of the ancient Greek poets, an eternal question underlay the action. What is the meaning of the everlasting conflict of good and evil? What, indeed, can be the ultimate purpose of life? Conan Doyle still found no answer to his lifelong search for the answers. When he rejected the dogmas of his Jesuit teachers, a void had been left that he felt compelled to fill.

During the bright autumn afternoons, Arthur rode across the heath on his own horse, Brigadier. The huge black gelding was named, of course, for the indomitable Étienne Gerard whose *Exploits,* running in *Strand Magazine,* had raised Conan Doyle's reputation to new heights.

Lottie and a friend, Jean Leckie, were Arthur's frequent riding companions. Jean was the daughter of a wealthy Scot from Blackheath who owned a home in nearby Sussex.

Though small and fragile-looking, with gold hair and green eyes, she was an accomplished horsewoman as well as a musician.

"Why either of you spend your time with an old man like me, I cannot see," Arthur decided in the wisdom of his thirty-eight years. "The young fellows these days must be blind as well as stupid!"

"We're particular, aren't we, Jean?" Lottie averred. Later she confided to her brother, "Jean is sympathetic, impulsive, completely feminine. But beneath the surface lies a character as strong as steel. T'will take an extraordinary man to win her love."

Arthur was taking lessons to perfect his riding so that he could hunt to the hounds, a favorite sport throughout the English countryside. His first experience only confirmed his distaste for shooting animals for sport.

"The childlike wail of a wounded hare is almost unbearable!" he told Touie.

"I wish you would write something that would show your readers what a lamb you are," she said fondly. "All your stories are violent or weird—often downright gruesome."

She had just finished reading proofs of her husband's latest historical work, *Uncle Bernac,* a sequel to *The Great Shadow.* Much of it was laid in Kirriemuir, the border country between Scotland and England where Doyle had visited James Barrie. There, it was conjectured, Napoleon had planned his invasion of the British Isles.

"Man is a complex creature, my dear," Arthur reminded her. "The many facets of his nature have inspired a poem in fact."

They were sitting in his crowded study beneath the larches. Arthur leaned over and drew from the clutter of manuscript on his desk a single sheet of paper and read:

There are others who are sitting,
Grim as doom,
In the dim ill-boding shadow
Of my room.
Darkling figures, stern or quaint,
Now a savage, now a saint,
Showing fitfully and faint
Through the gloom.

And those shadows are so dense,
There may be
Many—very many—more
Than I see.
They are sitting day and night
Soldier, rogue, and anchorite;
And they wrangle and they fight
Over me.

"I love your poetry, Arthur," exclaimed his wife. "You should publish it."

"I am preparing an anthology now," he assured her, "to be called *Songs of Action.*"

To please Touie, Conan Doyle did write a tale glorifying married love which he titled *A Duet, with Occasional Chorus.* The book pleased him more than any he had ever written; his public was divided. Still it was hailed by many, among them his old acquaintance, the draper's clerk, Herbert George Wells.

"My wife, for whose verdict I waited," wrote Wells, "has just finished the *Duet* . . . we both like it extremely. I've spent a year out of the last three years at a similarly 'commonplace' book. Still at it."

From H. G. Wells, the onetime science teacher who had skyrocketed to fame in 1895 with the publication of his *Time Machine,* this was treasured praise.

A number of old friends, like actor Henry Irving, dropped in at Undershaw. After two years, his portrayal of Corporal Gregory Brewster still evoked rafter-rocking applause. The handsome actor had a reputation for being ill-natured and difficult. Conan Doyle liked his razor wit, but went to any lengths to keep him away from a sharp-tongued neighbor and frequent visitor, lanky red-bearded Bernard Shaw.

Too often the first question from acquaintances and strangers was about Sherlock Holmes. All right, thought Arthur, I'll put him on the stage. He might score a great hit and help pay for this house.

The play, *Sherlock Holmes,* was sent first to Beerbohm Tree, actor-manager of Her Majesty's Theater, and second only in fame to Irving. Tree wanted to make the character of Sherlock Holmes over in the image of himself.

"Rather than rewrite it to make a different Holmes from mine, I will put it back in the drawer," Conan Doyle decided.

"Mr. Charles Frohman, the great American producer, is anxious to see the play," A. P. Watt, his literary agent, told him.

Frohman accepted the play at once and turned it over to his star, William Gillette, who also asked permission to rewrite it. By this time, Conan Doyle was so bored with the matter he agreed.

There was threat of war in Europe, and the Tsar of Russia had invited the powers to a peace conference at The Hague scheduled for January, 1899. Meetings were being held all over Europe in support of the proposals to limit armaments and set up an international court. Conan Doyle spoke at several meetings in Surrey in favor of the peace proposals.

Even as the world talked of peace and the crisis in Europe subsided, violence was brewing in the southernmost tip of Africa. Gold had been discovered in the Transvaal in 1886.

The Boer Republic had been overrun by fortune seekers whom the Dutch residents called "Uitlanders." Most of the newcomers were British. Since they paid taxes, they demanded a share in the government. Fearful of losing control of the Transvaal and her sister republic, the Orange Free State, President Kruger refused.

"Nobody asked you to come," he told complaining Englishmen. "You are always free to go if you do not like conditions here."

But gold held the Uitlanders. By May, 1899, their complaints became so loud that Her Majesty's government considered sending aid to her nationals in the Boer republics. With six thousand British territorials in nearby Natal and the Cape Colony, it was generally felt that two more divisions should set the matter right.

Arthur was not so sure. He had watched army maneuvers on Salisbury Plain. "The generals still set up our soldiers like tenpins!" he raged. "We haven't changed our tactics since Bunker Hill."

On Conan Doyle's fortieth birthday, William Gillette visited Undershaw to get the author's approval of his play script for *Sherlock Holmes*. Arthur drove to the railway station to meet his visitor in his two-horse landau. Holden, the groom, resplendent in a shiny new top hat, sat on the box.

The London train squealed to a stop, and out of a first-class carriage stepped Sherlock Holmes complete with long gray cape and deerstalker cap. Conan Doyle, who had never seen a photograph of Gillette, was thunderstruck to see a living image of his brainchild stalking along the platform.

"Dr. Watson, I presume!" The precise high-pitched voice was the voice of Holmes. Gillette stood beside the landau staring at an oversized and suitably astounded Watson. Neither man needed the mind of Sherlock Holmes to deduce who the other was.

Conan Doyle thought Gillette had written a fine play. In fact he liked everything about the actor. A gentleman by birth as well as manners, William Gillette had tremendous charm. By appearing as Holmes incarnate on the station platform, he had proved himself an able actor. The meeting was the beginning of a lifelong friendship.

In the Doyle family as in the world, 1899 was a year of upheaval. Arthur's youngest sister Dodo married an Episcopal clergyman named Cyril Angell. Connie's husband, William Hornung, scored a literary hit with *Raffles,* a sort of reverse Holmes in which the criminal was the hero. The book was dedicated to Conan Doyle. Innes, now a captain in the Royal Artillery, had gone out to India.

"I wish Lottie could go out for a holiday with Innes," begged Touie. "Lahore is one of the gayest cities in the Empire. She has been tied to me and the children too long."

So, in September, Arthur put Lottie aboard the S.S. *Egypt* bound for India. In Buffalo, New York, that November *Sherlock Holmes,* starring William Gillette, was a smash hit. While in South Africa, a world away, Boers, in canvas-covered ox-wagons, swept across the craggy passes into Natal to attack the thinly defended British positions. Boer riflemen, concealed in the boulder-strewn hills called *kopjes,* fought from deep trenches and shelter pits guarded by barbed wire.

"Most unorthodox!" complained the British as they retreated.

By November, nearly 11,000 British troops were hemmed in near Ladysmith. Their generals marched platoon after platoon in tight formation up the steep kopjes to storm the Boer entrenchments. They were mowed down in a blaze of rifle fire. In one "Black Week" in December, thousands of Tommies were slaughtered without a chance to fight back, bearing out Conan Doyle's assertion that British tactics were hopelessly antiquated.

All Britain was in an uproar. Many more than two divisions would be needed to bring peace to the Cape Colonies.

Arthur was an Empire man, a Unionist as in the days of the Irish rebellion. He could not endure the thought of Englishmen being pushed about. Off he went to enlist in the Middlesex Yeomanry.

The Colonel, a grizzled veteran, was puzzled what to do with the eager but middle-aged candidate.

"I presume you would want a commission," the enlisting officer pondered. "Can you ride and shoot?"

"Yes, in moderation."

"Have you any military experience?"

"A little in the Sudan."

"That was stretching it," Arthur admitted when recounting the story to friends. "But two white lies should be permitted a gentleman, to screen a woman or to get into a rightful fight."

The Ma'am did not think the war in South Africa was "a rightful fight." The British "pushed the Boers into an impossible position," she wrote angrily. "That awful gold is the root of the matter! If these politicians and journalists who so lightly drift into war had to go to the front, they would be more careful."

Nor did she think her son had any right to abandon his wife and children to enlist. "Your very height and breadth would make you a sure target!" she warned.

For once, Arthur defied her. The Boers had invaded British territory, he pointed out, making the question of "right" academic. "Either the British Empire has teeth or it hasn't. I have perhaps the strongest influence over young men, especially young sporting men, of anyone in England bar Kipling," he explained. "That being so, it is really important I give them a lead. I was honour-bound to be the first to volunteer."

The Middlesex Yeomanry, backed up by the War Office, decided Conan Doyle was too old for the ranks.

"Rubbish!" cried Arthur. When his friends John Langman and son Archie asked him to help organize a fifty-bed hospital, he jumped at the chance. Since he had not practiced medicine for so long, he would act as major-domo and troubleshooter for the outfit. They sailed for Africa aboard the transport *Oriental* on February 28, 1900.

The unit numbered fifty men including wardmasters, stewards, storekeepers and orderlies, and two fine young surgeons. The head surgeon, Dr. Robert O'Callagan, was a plump and fashionable gynecologist.

"Though I cannot imagine what use that specialty will be to him in war!" Conan Doyle commented to Charles Gibbs, one of the young doctors.

"Well, he's a personal friend of Langman's." Gibbs shrugged.

The trip south was uneventful except for a cricket match played against the Atlantic telegraph station on Cape de Verde Island. The team Arthur had patched together on the *Oriental* was the first to beat the telegraph men, who challenged each transport that passed.

The most difficult task of the voyage was trying to persuade the men to take an inoculation against enteritis. The tough Scottish regiments and hardened Tommies laughed at the medicos when they described the agonies of that virus. Less than 50 per cent submitted to the needle.

"They are more afraid of the shot than of the disease," opined Dr. Conan Doyle. "It should be compulsory."

By the time the *Oriental* reached Capetown, British troops were marching north into the Orange Free State. The capital, Bloemfontein, was captured, the rail line to the coast opened up. Troops from the *Oriental* and the Langman Hos-

pital Unit were among the first to make the all-day journey
from the port of East London in Natal.

The train roared across the African veldt, an expanse of
plains and flat-topped rocky kopjes. Little white farms, each
with its eucalyptus grove and dam, were scattered over the
veldt. When they passed across a makeshift bridge into the
Orange Free State, Arthur noted that many farmhouses flew
a white flag.

At night, huge fires along the track silhouetted the British
troops guarding their lifeline to the sea from Boer guerrillas.
As the train slowed to pass, the soldiers sang out: "Who are
you?"

"The Camerons," Arthur's carriage mates replied. Then
all the way down the line, fading off in the distance, he could
hear each regiment sing out its name.

"Wonderful is the atmosphere of war," he wrote in his
diary.

The hospital unit was dumped in a cricket field outside
Bloemfontein. A handsome pavilion, its stage, still set with
a garish scene from *H.M.S. Pinafore,* served as the main
ward. By evening the beds were up, and they were prepared
to receive patients.

Within two days casualties pouring in from the north
filled the fifty cots and overflowed on the floor mats in between. Then the stretcher bearers left the wounded on the
steps. Finally patients were scattered across the fields in
tents—more than three times the number the hospital unit
was prepared to care for. They lacked sufficient disinfectants,
linen or utensils.

Portly Dr. O'Callagan was incapacitated by the oppressive
heat of South Africa's rainy season, so Dr. Conan Doyle
plunged into doctoring as if he had never stopped. In a pink
undershirt to match his sun-reddened face, he set a pace to
challenge the younger surgeons. The sweat poured from

them. They barely had time for a wash, though behind the curtains on the gilt-framed stage they had set up a fine bath.

Then one evening, Dr. Conan Doyle went backstage for water. When he turned the tap not a drop fell.

"The Boers have taken the waterworks!" The disheartening news was all over town within the hour.

"Well, why don't the army buzz out and retake it?" he said. "It's only twenty miles away!"

But it was four long weeks before the army did retake the waterworks. Meanwhile, the overcrowded little capital was forced to use old wells. Almost forty thousand troops camped on the hot green veldt around Bloemfontein shared the insufficient and none too pure supply. An epidemic of enteritis broke out, and the area became a sinkhole of suffering and death. Wrapped in khaki blankets, the bodies were dumped into shallow graves—five thousand during April.

A haze of flies and nauseous odors hung over the Langman Hospital Unit. Emergency latrines were set up on the platform where the frivolous operetta set mocked the sufferers. Fashionable Dr. O'Callagan, unable to face such loathsome death, went home. An army doctor from Capetown, sent to replace him, took to the bottle. The hospital staff was further depleted when twelve of the fifteen orderlies fell ill. They were spunky little men from the Lancashire cotton mills who put up a good fight, but three died and the rest were so weakened they could not work.

"The Café Enterique may be forced to close its doors," warned Archie Langman.

The doctors had dubbed their pavilion the Café Enterique, Boulevard des Microbes. There was little that was humorous about it but the name.

"We must keep it going as long as this emergency lasts," insisted Dr. Conan Doyle, even though his rugged constitution was flagging.

By using Boer prisoners in the wards, the hospital continued to operate. They were decent quiet men, patient and kind to their suffering enemies. But the wards remained chaotic until one morning two Sisters of Mercy appeared to help.

"Angels from Heaven," Dr. Conan Doyle insisted, as miraculous order emerged.

On April 24, a blistering day at the end of the rainy season, word came that the waterworks were to be stormed. Conan Doyle and Archie Langman rode out behind the infantry. A few Boer horsemen could be seen in the distance. There was the occasional rat-a-tat of rifle fire. But there was no need to storm the works; there was no opposition.

14. ◆ *Sir Sherlock*

By August, 1900, Arthur was back in England. The strange war, the endless veldt and threatening kopjes, the enteric wards where many more men died than in battle—all seemed an unbelievable nightmare.

The war continued, but at Undershaw, little had changed. Mary and Kingsley had grown several inches while Touie was better than ever after a few months holiday in Naples with her mother.

"Lottie is having a marvelous time in Lahore!" she enthused. "I believe she has met someone special, too. With young Dodo married, she'd begun to feel like an old maid!"

"Lottie of the beautiful hair an old maid! Don't be silly, love!"

Arthur was immediately sorry for his outburst. He was tired. "In fact," he wrote Innes, "I feel damned sick!"

Before leaving South Africa, he and Archie Langman had ridden north with the British Army when it advanced on Pretoria, capital of the Transvaal. In a series of articles for *Strand Magazine* called "Days with the Army," he captured the sight, sounds and smell of the campaign.

. . . the heliographs signaling the advance from hill to hill along the thirty-mile front.

. . . the lines of red faces and khaki beneath bobbing sun helmets.

. . . the guns mounted on horse-drawn carriages, the choking dust, the smell of sweating men and horses.

. . . the young Guards' officers in their immaculate uniforms and polished putties mincing daintily across the steaming veldt as if they were walking in Mayfair.

He had seen the lines of British Tommies mowed down like so much wheat by the Boers' fast-firing rifles. He had seen the cavalry charge with only swords or sabers. He had seen the big guns unlimber in full view of an invisible foe. The waste was appalling.

"The lesson of war," he wrote, "is to have fewer soldiers who shall be very highly trained. . . . In this war the quick-firing rifle in the hands of a marksman has proved itself supreme."

The English press was clamoring for army reform, but Conan Doyle's suggestions, in "Some Military Lessons from The War," published in *Cornhill Magazine* in 1900, made army brass turn purple: No more marching into battle as if on parade. No more eye-catching uniforms and useless swords. Conceal artillery, using observation balloons to guide the fire. Teach the infantry to shoot; teach the cavalry to shoot.

"Every able-bodied youth and man in Great Britain must be taught to use a rifle," declared Conan Doyle.

"Democratize the Army!" agreed *The Daily News.*

Retired officers in their clubs spluttered with helpless rage. Young Guards' officers raised eyebrows so high that they dropped their monocles. The drill, the gold lace, the brave show . . . all to go!

Amid the storm of protest, Conan Doyle initiated the first rifle club at Undershaw. Men and boys from the whole county flocked in. They were outfitted with broad-brimmed hats turned up on one side, Australian-style, and fastened with a pin initialed U.R.C. Lying flat on the ground, they were taught to shoot at targets 600 yards away.

Meanwhile the war dragged on. Conan Doyle had to lay aside his history of the conflict, awaiting its outcome. To combat the Boers' guerrilla tactics, the British initiated a scorched earth policy. For their own protection, Dutch civilians were herded into camps when their land was laid waste.

"I have fought against all the savage tribes of Africa," cried President Kruger, now in exile, "but never any so savage as the British!"

Indignation swept across Europe like a tidal wave. The British Army was accused of starving the Boer farmers, raping their women, even of bayoneting babies. Some English papers repeated the stories of atrocities, ignoring their own press reports. Strong "stop the war" factions challenged the government's handling of the war.

That September, Conan Doyle was asked by the Liberal-Unionists to stand for Parliament in his home district of Edinburgh. Warned that he probably could not win in that Radical stronghold, he became more determined to give the opposition a run for their money. He had an overwhelming conviction that the present government must be supported.

"It would be a national disgrace and possibly an imperial disaster if we did not carry the Boer War to complete success," asserted Conan Doyle.

Winston Churchill, a fellow member of the Pall-Mall Club, agreed. Arthur had met Churchill in South Africa where he was a special correspondent for several papers. Only twenty-six, Winston Churchill was elected to Parliament in that first year of the twentieth century. Arthur Conan Doyle was defeated, but by less than a thousand votes.

Although "Mr. Sherlock Holmes" was a popular candidate, he was beaten by religion and the income tax. To meet the cost of war, the tax had been upped to a shilling on the pound. With extra duties on tobacco, beer and spirits, it was a crushing burden for the workingmen of Edinburgh. The opposition clinched the contest when they dug up Conan Doyle's Catholic background and flaunted it in that Protestant stronghold.

In January, 1901, Queen Victoria died. Stout, jolly Edward, at sixty a seemingly perennial Prince of Wales, succeeded to the throne.

Out in India, Lottie married Captain Leslie Oldham of the Royal Engineers. Arthur liked him from the moment he read his first stammering letter.

That April, Conan Doyle went up to Dartmoor in Devon, "the highest town in England," for a golfing holiday with a friend. They explored the lonely rock-strewn highland that was the moor, and later in front of the fire in the Princetown Hotel, his friend recounted ancient legends about the moor. There was one particular story about a giant animal which developed into *The Hound of the Baskervilles:*

> . . . a great, black beast, shaped like a hound, yet larger than any hound that ever mortal eye has rested upon . . . the thing tore the throat out of Hugo Baskerville. . . .

Conan Doyle wrote it as an unpublished early memoir of Sherlock Holmes. The legend of the phantom beast inspired a weird tale that overshadowed the eccentric detective. ". . . a real creeper!" Arthur described the new novel. Sir George Newnes and the stockholders of *Strand Magazine* were delighted.

"Holmes is at his best in *The Hound,*" Newnes exulted. "Couldn't you really bring him back? I'm not going to be happy until I know he's alive and back in his old rooms."

How could Arthur think of Sherlock Holmes when dreadful accusations were still being hurled against his England?

Protest meetings in Europe denounced the "savage" British in their dealing with the Boers. Even the London *Times* reprinted stories of disease and atrocity.

"Is there no one to deny these absurdities!" Conan Doyle complained. He was at a banquet given by his friend Sir Henry Thompson. "I know from personal experience the accusations are grotesque."

"Why don't you write a pamphlet and explain the matter in simple form," suggested his dinner partner. "The foreign office would certainly make its documents available to you."

"Such a defense should be translated into every language," mused Conan Doyle, intrigued by the idea. "What about costs of printing and distribution?"

"How much would you need for a start?"

"Perhaps a thousand pounds would suffice."

"Well, the project will take more than that—much more. But I can get that sum for you."

Conan Doyle was embarrassed that he had not caught his dinner companion's name.

"Sir Eric Barrington of the Foreign Office," his host told him. "What a stroke of luck if he will back the undertaking."

The project was blessed by fortune from the start. The publishing house of Smith, Elder and Company placed the whole machinery of their world-wide business at Conan Doyle's disposal. The public responded handsomely to the London *Times'* appeal for funds. In just nine days, on January 17, 1902, the pamphlet was ready for publication.

The Cause and Conduct of the War in South Africa was translated into every major European language. Even in Holland and Germany willing translators were found to present the English side of the story.

"The greater the opposition, the greater the need for the book," Conan Doyle insisted.

The strangest difficulties were encountered in Norway. A special foreword was attached to each country's edition. When the Norwegian edition was ready for press in Christiania, the foreword had not arrived. The translator lived a hundred miles from the city, and all the passes were blocked with snow. Conan Doyle's short address to the people of Norway was heliographed from peak to peak, and so found its way to press.

Conan Doyle had set out to change world opinion single-handedly. His pamphlet made friends and, surprisingly, money. The profits—more than twenty-five hundred pounds—could not be distributed to the subscribers, since many were anonymous. Old Soldiers' Institutes, Distressed Boers, and Doyle's pet Civilian Riflemen's Movement, now popular throughout England, were among the organizations that profited.

"A thousand pounds should be invested by Edinburgh University as a scholarship fund for a worthy South African student," Conan Doyle requested.

Imagining the fund would benefit either a Boer or a Briton, there was considerable surprise in the Bursar's office when the first recipient presented himself.

"I am a full-blooded Zulu," the young man explained.

His claim to the scholarship was indisputable.

As the war drew to a close, preparations were being made in London for the coronation of Edward VII. On the Coronation Honors List appeared the name of Dr. Conan Doyle. Touie and her mother as well as the children were so excited they talked of nothing else. When the new King invited the author of *The Cause and Conduct of the War* to a small dinner at Buckingham Palace, they all waited till after midnight for his return.

"Edward gave me the place of honor next to him," Arthur told his family. "We talked about my work."

"What's he like?"

"Stout, as you know, and rather inclined to be noisy. But he appears energetic and clearheaded. He won't be a dummy king," Conan Doyle opined. "He'll live to be over seventy, I should think."

"Can we see you knighted?" clamored Mary and Kingsley.

"I doubt that I shall accept a knighthood," Conan Doyle told his children. "Now off to bed."

"All my work for the state would seem tainted if I took a so-called reward," he explained to Touie.

"I understand your feeling," she assured him. "But what will you tell your mother?"

"I have never approved of titles," Arthur wrote the Ma'am. "The one I value is that of 'doctor' which was conferred by your self-sacrifice and determination."

Mrs. Doyle was horrified. To her, the spurs of knighthood were as real as they had been five centuries before.

"Has it not occurred to you," she demanded, "that to refuse a knighthood would be an insult to the King?"

She had used the one argument that could make Arthur change his mind.

On August 9, 1902, Arthur Conan Doyle traveled up to Buckingham Palace to be knighted. Among the candidates, he discovered Oliver Lodge, who shared his interest in psychic phenomena. Amid the pomp and ceremony, the two nearly forgot the honor being bestowed on them as they discussed the pros and cons of spiritual manifestations.

Although Sir Arthur complained, "They herded us into pens like so many prize pigs!" when he described the ceremony to his family, he could not help but feel pride as the messages of congratulations showered in.

"Your work during this terrible South African business was quite equal to that of a successful general," wrote one friend.

And from H. G. Wells, "Congratulations should go to those who have honored themselves by honoring you."

But another shadow was cast across his pleasure when some contemporary papers mentioned quite seriously that Conan Doyle doubtless owed his knighthood to the demon *"Hound"* who had just completed his triumphant run across the pages of the *Strand.* The month after he was knighted, he received a bill addressed to Sir Sherlock Holmes.

"I hope that I can stand a joke as well as anyone!" he roared. "But this is too much."

When challenged, a repentant clerk revealed that the joke had, in fact, been on him.

"My mates in the shop told me that you had been knighted, and that when a man was knighted he changed his name, and that you had taken that one."

"I feel like a new-married girl," Arthur wrote Innes, "who isn't sure of her own name! To add to the confusion, they've made me Deputy-Lieutenant of Surrey, which means nothing, so far as I can tell, except that I must buy an elaborate and expensive uniform that makes me look like a monkey on a stick!"

Sir Arthur Conan Doyle raised his eyes from the letter to the huge silver bowl on the desk in front of him, purchased by popular subscription and presented to him for his work during the Boer War and for his defense of his country afterward. He glowed with pleasure each time he read the inscription, most precious praise because it came from his fellow countrymen:

To Arthur Conan Doyle, Who, at Great Crisis—in Word and Deed—Served His Country

15. *The Real Sherlock Holmes*

A terrifying new sound shattered the peaceful silence of Hindhead in the spring of 1903. Calves and lambs ran bleating to their mothers. Horses kicked out and whinnied in fright. Dogs barked. Farmers waved pitchforks angrily. But most of the neighbors turned out to cheer as Sir Arthur Conan Doyle chugged along the country lane toward Undershaw in his ten-horsepower Wolseley.

Mary, now fourteen, and Kingsley, eleven, loved to sit on the high back seat of the Wolseley as it jounced along at breathtaking speeds of fifteen or twenty miles per hour. Innes, returned from the last of the fighting in South Africa, tried his hand at driving, as did Lottie and her new husband when they came to visit that summer. And the Ma'am, still spry and adventurous at seventy, could not get enough of motoring.

Fashionably outfitted in a long duster, broad-brimmed motoring hat and flowing veil, she sat in the tonneau like a queen holding court. One of the first times her son took her driving, they came upon a farm cart plodding up a hill. Arthur sounded his horn to pass. The horses reared, dumping turnips and cabbages all over the Wolseley. While the farmer and Conan Doyle argued, Mrs. Doyle sat unmoved

amid the vegetables, working at some knitting she had
brought along for just such an emergency.

The Ma'am had faith in her son's ability to operate a
motorcar, but when he told her he had resurrected Sherlock
Holmes she shook her head disapprovingly.

"You have forgotten the labor involved in a Holmes mystery," she reminded. "It has been ten years since you wrote
a short one."

"I am not conscious of failing powers," he retorted, angry
at the inference that his mind might have lost any acuteness
at forty-three. Certainly he was in top physical shape and
could still play cricket better than most younger men. "I
have already finished 'The Adventure of the Empty House.'
You will find that Holmes was never dead."

If Conan Doyle had any doubts himself as to his ability
to keep up his standard, they were dispelled when Sherlock
Holmes reappeared in the *Strand* that October. The crowds
at railway station bookstalls surpassed any bargain sale mob.
Sir George Newnes could not print copies fast enough. An
unbelievable offer of five thousand dollars per story came
from America.

Sir Arthur's defense of his country in the South African
war had made him one of the most famous men in the world.
Now there seemed little doubt he was one of the world's most
popular writers.

"Just as we suspected," gloated *The Westminster Gazette*.
"That fall over the cliff did not kill Holmes. In fact he never
fell. He climbed up the other side to escape his enemies."

The new series, *The Return of Sherlock Holmes*, introduced an older and more humble detective, who had known
both fear and failure. Some of the stories, notably "The Adventure of the Dancing Men," surpassed all the others.

Yet these very stories that made Conan Doyle the idol of

the "average" reader, young or old, were brushed aside as unworthy by the literary world.

"Give us *The White Company*, give us *Rodney Stone*. Conan Doyle is too big for the other sort of thing," grieved one literary magazine.

Conan Doyle agreed. He could not kill Holmes again, but he could retire him to a life of beekeeping and get on with more important work.

Sir Nigel was a long-dreamed-of companion book to *The White Company*. In describing the life and upbringing of Sir Nigel Loring, he might have been writing about himself —a poor lad of proud and ancient lineage, whose ancestral lands had been stolen, whose dearest companion was his ancient grandmother, Dame Ermentrude.

And Dame Ermentrude might have been the Ma'am, teaching the boy heraldry and chivalry beside the fire. Instilling in him high hopes and a fierce creed though he had not even a suit of armor.

In 1905 Edinburgh University awarded Sir Arthur an honorary LL.D. James Barrie, the most beloved playwright in Britain, notably for *The Admirable Crichton* and his latest fantasy, *Peter Pan*, was among the many friends and admirers who flocked to see him honored.

"Your talents are diverse, old boy," Barrie assured him with usual candor, "but it's for Sherlock Holmes you'll be remembered!"

H. G. Wells expressed a similar opinion when he visited Undershaw the following summer. Sir Arthur had built a miniature monorail on the grounds, inspired by Wells' newest novel, *A Modern Utopia,* in which he predicted England would one day be laced with the single-railed trains. Doyle's model, driven by electricity and steadied with a gyroscope, had carriages large enough for the children. Mary and Kingsley, big teen-agers though they were, whooped with the joy of it.

"I cannot understand how you could conceive half a dozen mysterious plots in as many weeks!" marveled Wells. "And all plausible."

Sir Arthur chuckled. "Nor can I understand how you weave such elaborate forecasts of the future. But I intend to try it one day, and beat you at your own game," he warned.

"Seriously though," he continued as the two men walked away from the shouting children toward the house, "a number of problems have come my way similar to those I have invented. Sometimes, I admit, Holmes' semiscientific methods are labored and slow compared to practical police methods. Only the other day there was a burglary at the village inn. The constable, with no theories, seized the culprit while I had got no further than that he was left-handed and wore hobnailed boots!"

"Ah, but the constable knew just which of the villagers would be apt to commit petty thievery," reminded Wells. "What about a crime not so ordinary?"

The two authors found a shady place beneath the larches outside Sir Arthur's study and lit their pipes. The gardens they overlooked were alive with fragrant blooms. The flowers bobbed and danced to the soft tinkling of the piano as Touie ran lazily over some gay little dance tunes.

"Two cases have come to my attention in the last month," mused Conan Doyle, "similar to the disappearing bridegroom in 'A Case of Identity.' One I am not at liberty to discuss. A neighbor's daughter was engaged to a young foreigner who disappeared quite suddenly. The grief-stricken girl appealed to me for help. I was able, by deduction, to show her clearly not only where he had gone but how unworthy he was of her affection."

"How do you begin?" wondered the science-fiction expert.

"In cases of this kind, I begin with the premise that no person can disappear completely unless he wants to. Usually there is little enough to go on. But recently I had complete success in locating a man who vanished after drawing his bank balance amounting to forty pounds.

"Relatives contacted me after the police had been on the case for a week. They feared he had been murdered for the money. The man had gone up to London from his country home and checked in at one of the larger hotels. After completing his business, he went to a music hall, returning to the hotel early—about ten P.M. Next morning his evening dress was found in his room, but he was gone. A guest in an adjoining room claimed to have heard him moving about during the night."

"That's the whole story?"

"That's the whole of it. I replied to his anxious relatives by return mail that the missing man was evidently in either Glasgow or Edinburgh, though in the week that had passed he might have moved to another part of Scotland. I suggested the police search in small remote villages."

"He was found?"

"Just as I deduced." Conan Doyle smiled. "There I should leave the matter. 'You have all the facts,' Holmes would say, 'You know my methods. Apply them.'"

Wells looked crestfallen. "I wouldn't know how to start!"

"The first thing is to examine the testimony and separate what is certain from what is conjecture," explained Conan Doyle. "One bit of testimony in this case rang false. How could a guest in a big busy hotel be sure that sounds he heard came from the room next door? I decided to disregard his statement.

"The fact that the man drew all his money out of the bank confirmed my opinion that he meant to disappear. It seemed clear that he left the hotel during the night. Why, I asked myself, was he not noticed by the night porter? He must have left between eleven thirty and midnight," I decided, "when the hall and lobby were full of returning theater-goers. Clearly he meant to catch a train to take him away. But where? If he were deposited at a provincial station in the early morning, he would surely be noticed by the station-master. Yet the fact that he abandoned his dress suit indicated he was bound for a rural community where he would no longer need it."

"So how does that bring us to Glasgow or Edinburgh?"

"Our man's destination had to be a large terminus where all passengers would disembark, and he would be lost in the crowd. The timetable told me that two expresses for Scotland left near midnight. One of them was certainly his goal."

"Astounding, my dear Holmes!" exclaimed H. G. Wells.

That August, 1905, officers of the northern squadron of the French battle fleet paid an official visit to England.

"Who would you like most to see?" Admiral Caillard was asked.

"His Majesty the King and the Grand Admiral Sir John Fisher, of course," was the prompt reply, "and Sir Arthur Conan Doyle."

Sir Arthur's reception for the visitors was a complete suc-cess, but Undershaw was never to see such gaiety again.

That winter the feeble spark of life that sustained Touie wavered. By June, she was much worse. Arthur called in specialists from London, but they could offer little hope. Still he would not give up.

"T. holds her own well," he wrote in his daily bulletin to Innes at the Staff College in Bedford.

And next day, "Touie better. Sat up for tea. I hope for the best."

Finally, "It may be days or weeks, but the end now seems

inevitable. She is without pain, and easy in her mind. She is taking it all with her usual sweet and gentle equanimity. She is the most cheerful and unselfish person any of us will ever know."

The day before she died, Touie seemed to sense that the end was near. "I hope your father will marry again," she told Mary.

Lady Louise Conan Doyle passed away quietly at three in the morning of July 4, 1906. Her frail hand rested confidingly in her husband's—those big capable hands that had literally sustained her life for so many years.

16. Wedding Bells for Sherlock Holmes

Arthur seldom suffered anything more serious than a toothache. Off Africa, he had defeated the blackwater fever, a killer of white men; even the dreaded enteric virus had only slowed him down. But when Touie died, he became seriously ill. Insomnia and general weakness made work impossible.

"Nerves," pronounced Dr. Charles Gibbs, Conan Doyle's medical adviser since South African days.

Arthur went off to the North Sea Coast of his native Scotland to hide his grief in a lonely inn near Dunbar. Not until Christmas was he stirred to action by a bundle of press clippings sent him by his secretary. They concerned a crime already three years old—a crime whose sinister nature intrigued the mind of Sherlock Holmes. The accompanying letter from the accused man was a cry for help that touched the heart of Sir Arthur Conan Doyle.

On August 18, 1903, George Edalji was arrested and charged with maiming and killing a pony at the Great Wyrley Colliery in Staffordshire. In the six months preceding the arrest, there had been a series of animal mutilations. Armed with a razor-sharp instrument, the killer inflicted a long shallow wound which caused a spurt of blood but did not pierce the vital organs. The unfortunate beasts died a slow agonizing death.

The maimings were accompanied by anonymous letters of a particularly vicious nature. The writer accused a number of local residents as accomplices, described vividly the joys of ripping up cattle, and issued horrid threats.

"There will be merry times in Wyrley in November," the last letter warned, "when they start on little girls. . . ."

The accused, George Edalji, was the son of the Vicar of Great Wyrley. Thirty-four years old at the time of his arrest, he was a respected Birmingham lawyer, recipient of the Birmingham Law Society's Bronze Medal in 1898.

"Why," Conan Doyle asked himself, "has so unlikely a person been accused of the senseless crimes?"

One answer seemed evident. The father, the Reverend Shapurgi Edalji, was a Parsee, an Indian married to an English woman. Though a Church of England clergyman, the Reverend Edalji was, to the simple folk of Great Wyrley, a "Black Man," distrusted and feared. His frail brown-skinned son George had always been blamed for every prank occurring in the village.

Conan Doyle detested religious intolerance. But to be prejudiced toward a man because of his color, he considered senseless and cruel. He studied all the accounts of the trial. Described by many newsmen as "an incredible tragedy," the evidence against Edalji was circumstantial, unprovable and riddled with contradictions. And what, above all, was the reason for the insane acts?

"Many and wonderful were the theories," wrote one Birmingham reporter, "as to why Edalji had gone forth in the night to slay cattle. The widely accepted idea was that he made nocturnal sacrifices to strange gods."

"The son of a Church of England clergyman! Bah!" Conan Doyle brushed aside the newspapers and picked up

George Edalji's letter. During the three years the man had been in prison the cattle maimings had continued, right up until his release, late in 1906—release but no pardon.

"So what am I to do now?" wrote the ex-convict. "I have been struck off the roll of solicitors . . . could hardly practice my profession while still under the supervision of the police. Am I innocent or guilty? They won't tell me."

Oh, won't they? thought Conan Doyle, and wrote George Edalji to meet him in a London hotel.

Arthur immediately recognized Edalji, who was reading a newspaper which he held close to his eyes and a little sideways. He did not see Conan Doyle until the well-known face looked right down at him.

"Mr. Edalji," the former eye specialist stated, "you suffer from astigmatic myopia, I see. Why don't you wear glasses?"

The young man peered up at Conan Doyle nervously. Sir Arthur patted his shoulder reassuringly.

"I've gone to two ophthalmic surgeons, Sir Arthur," George Edalji replied. "I cannot be fitted for glasses that would be any help."

"Why was this fact not brought out at the trial?"

"My advisers thought the evidence against me so ridiculous that it was not necessary."

"And so it appears to be," Sir Arthur decided.

"The Case of Mr. George Edalji" began running in *The Daily Telegraph* in January, 1907. With Holmsian care, Sir Arthur Conan Doyle had retraced the whole case. Systematically he tore down every bit of evidence the police had used to build a case against Edalji.

"These wrongs would have been comic had they not been so tragic! If the whole land had been raked, I do not think that it would have been possible to find a man who was so unlikely, and indeed so incapable, of committing such bloody and brutal crimes."

Conan Doyle had sent Edalji to an eye specialist in London who found the myopia worse than expected. "He could not recognize anyone at six yards!"

Yet this man was supposed to have crept from his father's room in the dead of night, made his way across slag heaps, railway yards and mineheads, slashed a pony, and returned by an even more roundabout route—in the dark!

"Presposterous," insisted Conan Doyle. "I tried it myself in broad daylight and found it hard going across rails, wires and other obstacles."

His articles caused such public indignation that the government appointed a committee to review the case. Edalji was cleared of the crime, but still blamed for the anonymous letters.

The most absurd charge of all, thought Conan Doyle. If he'd been tried on that charge, it would not have stood up in court.

After months of investigation, Conan Doyle could name the real criminal. Bit by bit he had built up his case against a schoolmate of George Edalji's, and had carefully documented evidence to back up his theory.

Conan Doyle had procured specimens of his suspect's handwriting which an expert testified was the same as in the letters. He had, besides, received seven letters himself, threatening, in the foulest language, all kinds of horrible vengeance unless he ceased his investigation.

To top it all, he had got hold of the murder weapon—a horse lancet—which the murderer had learned to use while working aboard a cattle boat.

The Home Office ignored the new evidence. When Conan Doyle's new series of articles, "Who Wrote the Letters," began in *The Daily Telegraph*, the Staffordshire police wrote him a sorrowful letter accusing him of libeling an innocent man.

"An innocent man!" roared Sir Arthur, "—who has already been convicted several times for damage, arson and stealing!"

He was resting at the home of his old friends, the Leckies, in Blackheath.

"At least the Law Society has shown its contempt for officialdom by readmitting Edalji to the roll of solicitors," reminded Mr. Leckie. His righteous wrath had been thoroughly aroused by Arthur's tales of the harassment of the unfortunate vicar and his family.

"I am completely disillusioned," confessed Conan Doyle. "Government appears to be an unavowed trade union. The members will admit nothing incriminating about another official regardless of the misery to their helpless victims."

"You've done your best, Arthur," soothed Jean Leckie, "let's go for a canter."

The awakening earth scented the soft May air as Arthur and Jean rode off across the greening heath. Now thirty-four, Jean was at the height of her beauty. Her golden hair bobbed gaily beneath her black riding hat. To Arthur, it was like a flag of joy signaling an end to his winter of sorrow.

During the months that followed, Jean was his constant companion and was an enthusiastic spectator at all Arthur's cricket matches. They dined in London and went to the theater. She even persuaded him to attend an occasional concert, though he claimed no understanding of music. She played both piano and harp expertly.

They went on a number of beach excursions that summer. One evening in August he brought out a ukelele on which he had laboriously learned to plunk "Love's Old Sweet Song." Jean clapped enthusiastically.

"A musician I will never be," Arthur admitted. "But if you'd have me, I would be a devoted husband."

"I think I've always loved you, Arthur," Jean told him. "There never could have been anyone else."

On September 18, 1907, Sir Arthur Conan Doyle married Miss Jean Leckie in St. Margaret's Church, Westminster. At the reception in the Hotel Métropole's Whitehall Rooms, over two hundred old friends waited to greet them. Perhaps the happiest wedding guest of all was George Edalji. Not only had he been acquitted, but the publicity Sir Arthur's investigation had directed to his case had helped to speed the establishment of a Court of Criminal Appeal.

Arthur took Jean to the Mediterranean for their honeymoon—to Egypt, Greece and Turkey. The aging Sultan, a Holmes fan, sent a message to Sir Arthur apologizing for not greeting him personally. It was, he explained, the Holy Month, Ramadan. He presented Conan Doyle with the Order of the Medjedie, and Jean with the Order of the Chevekat.

After years devoted to the care of others, Arthur now discovered the joy of being cared for. He had bought a new home in Sussex, near Jean's family, and leased a flat in London at 15 Buckingham Palace Mansions. Jean managed both households with quiet efficiency. She took charge as well of many business details and screened his visitors carefully.

Arthur was so proud of her skill as a hostess that he began to enjoy entertaining once more. The billiard room of the new mansion, "Windlesham," ran the full length of the house with a wall of windows at each end. Paintings lined the walls, among them Sidney Paget's portrait of Sir Arthur himself. When the rugs were cleared away, one hundred and fifty couples could dance in that room. But when the fires were lit, and the gas mantles glowed, it was a cozy room for chatting. Notables from all over the world visited the Doyles there—Vilhjalmur Stefansson, the Arctic explorer, Rudyard Kipling, actors, writers, statesmen. In one cozy alcove, the famous American detective William Burns talked well into the night about his days with the United States Secret Service and with Allan Pinkerton's Detective Agency. His adventures inspired a new Holmes novel, *The Valley of Fear.*

The restlessness that had plagued Arthur most his life left him. He did not even have much desire to work. To please Jean he wrote two short Sherlock Holmes stories, "Wisteria Lodge" and "The Bruce-Partington Plans." Since she loved gardening, he tried his hand at it. When she asked him to prepare a bed for some prize roses, he sent the dirt flying.

"Dearest," she warned, "you are digging a garden not excavating for a tunnel!"

In March, 1909, Sir Arthur presided at a centenary dinner honoring the birth of Edgar Allen Poe. Though he revered Poe's memory, Conan Doyle's mind was far from the banquet room. Jean was expecting a baby that month.

"I'm no novice as a father," he confided to Innes, "but the prospect disturbs me more than I care to confess. Jean is tiny, and not young to bear her first child."

"All will be well," Innes assured his brother.

Denis Percy Stewart Conan Doyle arrived on schedule. In November of the following year, Jean presented Arthur with another son, Adrian Malcolm. The second name honored her favorite brother, Dr. Malcolm Leckie; Arthur chose the first because he fancied it.

Arthur Conan Doyle was fifty years old. Only faint streaks of gray in his hair and mustache betrayed the passing years. The future stretched before him, a vista of peace and joy.

17. The Pen Is Mightier

In the changing world of the twentieth century, Sir Arthur's pen was his knightly sword in a number of battles. His causes were diverse, from divorce law reform to the rules governing the Olympic Games.

In 1909, he took up his pen in anger over Belgian administration of the Upper Congo. Deep in that jungle colony was a fortune in rubber and ivory if the natives could be forced to bring it out. For years, English traders, consuls and missionaries had reported that agents of King Leopold of Belgium tortured and flogged the Africans to make them work harder. They had seen the chicote in action, a whip of hippopotamus hide that ripped the flesh into wire patterns.

In 1903, Great Britain protested. "Humanity and fair wages" was the cry.

A three-day debate in Brussels commanded the world's attention, and a Congo Reform Association was formed. When Conan Doyle became convinced that unspeakable tortures were being used to keep the natives in line, he threw himself into the fight.

The Crime of the Congo was first published in October, 1909. The sixty-thousand-word report was fully documented with facts and figures, believable only because of disinterested eyewitness reports.

160 THE REAL SHERLOCK HOLMES

"I am convinced," Sir Arthur wrote in his introduction, "that the reason public opinion has not been more sensitive upon the question of the Congo, is that the terrible story has not been brought home to the public."

"I am very glad," wrote Winston Churchill, President of the Trade Board, "that you have turned your attention to the Congo. I will certainly do what I can to help you."

The outcry against Congo atrocities welled to thunder.

"Yet it was not his book—excellent as it was—" opined a fellow worker, "or his manly eloquence on the platform, nor the influence he wielded in rallying influential men to our cause. . . . It was just the fact that he was—Conan Doyle; and that he was with us. His whole personality appeals to the finest and most robust qualities of the English race."

That same year, Conan Doyle set out to solve another real murder mystery. Oscar Slater was sentenced to hang in Glasgow for the brutal murder of a wealthy old lady, Miss Marion Gilchrist. The day before he was to die, May 27, his sentence was changed to life imprisonment, and he disappeared into dreary Peterhead prison. There he might have rotted, but for Conan Doyle.

Slater's lawyers asked Sir Arthur to intervene in the case. The court had never been able to prove any connection between Slater and his victim. The slim evidence on which the police built their case against him was one diamond brooch he pawned in order to buy passage to the United States. Miss Gilchrist's maid could not be sure that it had even belonged to her mistress.

"The man is an unsavory person," Arthur wrote his mother, "crude morally. But a thief and a murderer he is not. I believe his conviction to be a monstrous miscarriage of justice."

Sir Arthur launched a press campaign climaxed by the publication of his booklet, *The Case of Oscar Slater,* published in 1912. As in the case of Edalji, he tore the evidence against Slater to bits, then advanced a new theory. Slater's motive for murder had been stated as robbery. But ". . . was the assassin after the jewels at all?" wondered Conan Doyle.

After battering in the victim's head, the murderer had gone to the bedroom and lit the gas. He did not touch the valuable rings and watch lying on the dressing table. Instead he broke open and rifled a wooden box which contained Miss Gilchrist's private papers. They were scattered all over the room.

With Holmsian logic, Conan Doyle built up his case that the murderer must have been known to his victim or she would never have opened the door to him—a relative perhaps, after her will or some other precious document.

Sir Arthur rallied newspapers and even the cautious *Law Journal* to Slater's cause. But the identity of the man who bashed in the old lady's skull as well as the weapon used remained a riddle. And Oscar Slater remained within the gloomy walls of Peterhead prison.

Conan Doyle was not always a crusader. He dramatized *Brigadier Gerard* in 1909; later that year *Fires of Fate,* the dramatic version of *The Tragedy of Korosko,* was a sell-out.

"I believe I can conquer the theater," Conan Doyle said to Lewis Waller, who had been his partner as well as star actor in the last two ventures. "I want to dramatize my novel of the Regency era, *Rodney Stone.*"

"A play about boxing! No manager will touch it."

Lewis Waller had long been actor-manager of the Imperial Theater and knew the business well. After reading the script Conan Doyle showed him, he was more convinced it could never succeed. "Seven sets—forty-three speaking parts. Why it would be outrageously expensive. Impossible!"

To Conan Doyle "impossible" was like a red flag to a bull.

" Think of the spectacle! A panorama of sporting England in 1812. I could call it *In the Days of the Regents.*"

Waller still shook his head. So Conan Doyle took the gamble himself. Leasing the Adelphi Theater, he produced a play called *The House of Temperley,* which had, indeed, some realistic fight scenes, a little anemic love interest, even a battle scene. The audiences loved it. Yet after four months of dwindling attendance, the play had to close. The final blow was the sudden death of King Edward VII on May 6, 1910. Theater lights went out all over London.

Conan Doyle had leased the Adelphi for six months, with expenses of six hundred pounds a week. He wrote a new play in a week, cast it and went into rehearsal. A month after the King's death, on June 4, the Adelphi's marquee shone again for *The Speckled Band,* based on an early Holmes adventure of the same name.

Sherlock Holmes and Dr. Watson worked their old magic. *The Speckled Band* more than made up its author's losses. Besides its long run in London, two touring companies were on the road by September.

With success, Conan Doyle turned from the theater to another challenge. H. G. Wells' prophetic books were enjoying tremendous popularity.

"Yet he is not truly psychic," mused Conan Doyle. He was sitting in the great Viking chair that had been presented to him by the Danish government when he visited Copenhagen the year before to attend Innes' wedding to a Danish girl, Clara Schwensen. Jean had placed the handsome piece beside the fireplace in an alcove of the billiard room.

"I would like to do for science fiction what Holmes has done for the detective tale," he decided.

In his mind were several of his medical school teachers— the squat figure of Professor Rutherford with his Assyrian beard and overpowering voice; and scrawny little Crum

Brown, frightened of his own chemical concoctions; stern, retiring Turner, who had taught himself anatomy.

Out of his musings emerged barrel-chested, bull-headed Professor Challenger, the merriest, maddest genius ever to invade the pages of a book. Everything about him was over-powering, like his voice—especially his aversion to reporters and ringing telephones that interrupted his work. Kind-hearted as he was gruff, in the name of science he would not hesitate to bite the housekeeper to note her reaction.

Professor Summerlee was Challenger's opposite—little, skinny, apparently timid, but as devoted to science and militant about his own ideas. Together they marched up the Amazon, arguing all the way, into *The Lost World* and into the hearts of Conan Doyle fans. With them went one favored reporter, Edward Malone, and Lord Roxton, big game hunter and perfect English gentleman, to find, atop a plateau deep in the jungle, prehistoric life preserved complete with brontosauri and apemen.

So excellent was Conan Doyle's report of the expedition that six months after publication of *The Lost World* a party of scientists from the University of Pennsylvania set out for Brazil to "seek Conan Doyle's 'lost world' or some scientific evidence of it."

"You don't think they took your book seriously, Arthur!" exclaimed Jean in horror.

"Of course not. But they're bound to find something of interest."

The Lost World was imaginary fun. Its sequels, *The Poison Belt, The Disintegrator Machine, The Day the World Screamed,* were written in a more serious vein. They seemed disturbingly prophetic, especially in the year 1912.

For a long time, Sir Arthur, like many Englishmen, did not believe that Germany was a menace to Great Britain. After all, the King and the Kaiser were cousins.

"And what could Germany gain by picking a quarrel with us?" argued Conan Doyle.

As a member of the Anglo-German Society for the Improvement of Relations, he worked tirelessly for friendship between the two nations. Yet the rumors grew more persistent as Germany continued to build up her High Seas Fleet. Conan Doyle began to conjecture what the next war might be like.

"The real danger lies in the submarine and the airship," he wrote in a series of articles, titled *England in the Next War,* for the *Fortnightly Review,* published in 1913.

Balloons, once used for observation in war, for sport in times of peace, had been brought to menacing proportions by Count Von Zeppelin. The powered airship could travel far greater distances than any aeroplane.

"They will not be affected by a blockade," Conan Doyle pointed out. "Nor will the submarine . . .

> What exact effect a swarm of submarines, lying off the mouth of the Channel and the Irish Sea, would produce upon the victualling of these islands is a problem which is beyond my conjecture [the author admitted]. Other ships besides the British would be likely to be destroyed, and international complications would probably follow.

One solution he suggested was a Channel tunnel connecting England and France; two hundred feet below the Channel at its narrowest point, between Dover and Calais, the tunnel must be twenty-six miles long. With modern engineering methods, he thought it might be completed in three years—if, he warned, three years is not already too long.

Sir Arthur drew strong support for his plan, but most officials, including the Prime Minister, believed England could still rely on her "Invincible Navy" to keep communications open.

Conan Doyle followed up his articles with a prophetic novel called *Danger*. In it, he imagined a tiny country called Norland bringing Great Britain to her knees by the strategic use of a small fleet of submarines. He predicted that English merchant ships armed as auxiliary cruisers would learn to zigzag to avoid torpedoes, but only aircraft would be effective against the underwater raider. At the end of the book the submarine *Iota* sinks one of England's biggest ocean liners, the *Olympic*, off Land's End, and the English government asks for an armistice.

In submitting the novel to *Strand*, Conan Doyle asked editor Greenhough Smith to query naval experts. "Could this happen?"

"I am compelled to say that I think it most improbable," commented Admiral Sir Compton Domville, K.C.B., "and more like one of Jules Verne's stories than any other author I know."

"I do not myself think that any civilized nation will torpedo unarmed and defenseless merchant ships," agreed Admiral Penrose Fitzgerald.

Danger began running in *Strand* in July, 1914. Sir Arthur Conan Doyle and his wife had just returned from a month's tour of Canada as guests of the government.

They had left the children—Denis, Adrian and the toddler Lena Jean, born in December, 1912—in the capable hands of a governess, with Mary, good-looking and efficient at twenty-five, as housekeeper. Kingsley, a handsome athlete of twenty-two, was preparing to take his medical degree at St. Mary's Hospital in London, but he found time to keep his small half-brothers amused.

While the trip had been spent in sightseeing, Sir Arthur was always so besieged by reporters that he was glad at last to return home.

On June 28, as the liner *Megantic* bore them across the

calm summer waters of the North Atlantic, a pistol was fired twice in faraway Sarajevo, capital of Bosnia. Archduke Francis Ferdinand and his wife Sophie slumped against each other as their big touring car sped away from the crowds that had come to greet them. Reverberations from those shots toppled the countries of the world, one by one, into the maelstrom of war.

18. *The Great War*

And now I turn to the war [Conan Doyle wrote in his diary], the physical climax of my life as it must be of the life of every living man and woman. Each was caught as a separate chip and swept into that fearsome whirlpool, where we all gyrated for four years, some sinking for ever, some washed up all twisted and bent, and all showing in our souls and bodies some mark of the terrible forces which had controlled us so long.

Between August and September, 1914, the best troops of seven warring nations clashed in Flanders' fields. Walking in his garden at Windlesham, Sir Arthur Conan Doyle could hear the distant rumble of artillery, if the wind was right. The Germans marched steadily across Belgium. Friends and countrymen were dying. Innes, now Colonel Doyle, a staff officer with the 24th Division, and Malcolm Leckie, a captain in the Royal Army Medical Corps, were both in the firing-line.

Sir Arthur wrote the War Office in desperation. "I am not young, and long out of practice, but couldn't I help with the wounded?"

The War Office politely turned him down.

Malcolm Leckie was killed in August. In September,

Kingsley joined the Royal Army Medical Corps and marched away with the First Hampshires.

To aid the war effort, Sir Arthur organized the first Home Guard. It was publicized all over England, and after two weeks was formally reorganized as the Crowborough Company of the Sixth Royal Sussex Volunteer Regiment, with a retired army officer in command. Sir Arthur remained a contented full private throughout the war.

Jean threw herself into the organization of a home for Belgian refugees. Mary was making shells for Vickers, where titled dowagers and cultured young ladies competed to see who could turn out the most shell cases.

In the gray, blustery dawn of September 22, 1914, the German submarine U-9 revolutionized naval warfare by sending three British cruisers—*Aboukir, Cressy* and *Hogue* —to the bottom of the North Sea. In little more than an hour, Kapitanleutnant Otto Weddigen and his crew of 20 men had destroyed 36,000 tons of battleship; 1,400 of the 2,250 complement of British navy men were lost.

"More than the loss during the whole Battle of Trafalgar!" exclaimed Sir Arthur when he heard of the tragedy. To the author of *Danger* the news was hardly as incredible as it seemed to the British Admiralty and even to Admiral Alfred Von Tirpitz, father of Germany's modern navy.

As naval experts across the world hurried back to their drawing boards to design bigger and better undersea craft, Sir Arthur found a different lesson in the dreadful tragedy. Since battleships carried few lifeboats, the survivors had saved themselves by clinging to petrol cans and other floating debris. They told of listening helplessly to the cries of their comrades as they grew too weak and numb to keep themselves afloat. Most of the men lost were drowned in the frigid waters of the North Sea before help could reach them.

"Surely," Sir Arthur wrote *The Daily Mail* and *Chronicle,* "it is possible to provide each man with protection, if only a rubber belt or collar?"

Within a few days, the Admiralty ordered a quarter of a million Indian rubber collars that seamen could carry in their pockets and blow up themselves. Henceforth, the device would be part of each man's equipment.

But as winter approached, it became apparent that the lifesaving collar only prolonged the agony when seas were high and icy cold. On the last night of that fateful year 1914, the battleship *Formidable* was torpedoed in the English Channel. There were few survivors.

On January 2, Sir Arthur wrote *The Daily Chronicle* suggesting the use of inflatable rubber boats.

"We can spare and replace the ships," he insisted. "We cannot spare the men."

Then in April, off the Old Head of Kinsale near Land's End, a giant ocean liner, the *Lusitania,* was torpedoed by the U-20. Of the nearly 2,000 persons aboard, 1,198 perished, many of them women and children. Charles Frohman, who first produced the play *Sherlock Holmes,* was lost with 124 other Americans. All Conan Doyle's predictions were fulfilled but one. England did not ask for a negotiated peace.

Thoroughly aroused by the senseless brutality, the British Navy pulled out the stops on its own underseas campaign, while across the Channel, the long butchery in the trenches began.

During that spring, a friend whose brother had been taken prisoner complained to Sir Arthur that censorship prevented him from sending war news.

"Sherlock Holmes is an expert on secret messages," he remarked. "Surely he could devise some method of getting news to our boys in Magdeburg Prison Camp!"

Conan Doyle used the simple ruse of putting needle pricks under printed letters in one of his books to spell out a message. Assuming the censor would examine the first chapters, he began his bulletin in the third. An accompanying letter explained: "The book is rather slow opening, but might interest you from Chapter III on."

The book went through all right, but its recipient missed the clue altogether. He was, however, delighted to have one of Conan Doyle's books, and loaned it to several fellow prisoners. One of them was sharp enough to find the message. Word came back that they hoped Conan Doyle would mail more books. So each month, Sir Arthur pricked out his news bulletin until he learned that the prisoners were allowed British papers.

Sherlock Holmes himself came out of retirement to aid the British Secret Service. In "His Last Blow," he disguised himself as Mr. Altamont of Chicago to trap Germany's most clever spy. He tells Watson sadly:

> There is an east wind coming, a wind such as never blew on England yet . . . many of us may wither before its blast. But it's God's own wind none the less, and a cleaner, better, stronger land will lie in the sunshine when the storm has cleared.

Holmes' creator, like fellow Englishmen, clung to that hope through the weary months and years.

Kingsley had won a commission and was taking a bombing course at Lyndhurst. Oscar Hornung, Connie and Willie's only son, had been killed, as well as Lottie's husband Major Oldham. She was in Yorkshire with the Ma'am waiting to go to Europe to join the French Red Cross.

On the battle lines, poison gas was a new horror, but the continuing toll taken by shrapnel and bullet concerned Sir Arthur more. Brigade after brigade lost half their men in attempts to storm German positions. Conan Doyle wrote several articles to the London *Times* suggesting armor for the troops.

"The bullet-proof man and the torpedo-proof ship are two great ideals," agreed Winston Churchill, now First Lord of the Admiralty.

The Minister of Munitions replied: "Sir Arthur, there is no use arguing here, for there is no one in the building who does not know that you are right. The whole difficulty lies in making the soldiers accept your views."

Conan Doyle admitted there was a limit to what a man could carry. "But the helmet is not enough, for it only deflects bullets downward," he pointed out. "How about shoulder guards? Could strong breastplates be kept in the trenches for temporary use?"

The armored tank was the answer. Conan Doyle credited its use with the winning of the war. And much credit for its invention he gave to Winston Churchill.

In 1916, the Foreign Office asked Conan Doyle to visit the Western front as special press attaché. Besides the speeches and articles for the government, he was preparing a history of the British campaign in France and Flanders based on detailed information given him by the commanding generals. He jumped at the opportunity to see the war firsthand.

Within twelve hours after leaving home, he was in the front lines in Flanders. He stumbled and slipped along ten miles of rough clay trenches that first morning. Everywhere he was greeted enthusiastically by cheerful Tommies, some so young they looked liked grimy tattered boys just off the cricket field. Overhead a British aeroplane circled lazily.

The great desolate area that was the Western front was marked off by sausage-shaped observation balloons. Only an occasional rat-tat of machine-gun fire or the whistle of a sniper's bullet broke the awful silence.

Innes, with whom Conan Doyle spent a night, took him to

see the Ypres salient, a huge semicircle of horror. When he left, Arthur carried in his pocket his brother's instructions about the care of his wife Clara and their one small son, now living at Windlesham—"should anything happen to me."

Traveling east near a village Conan Doyle thought was Mailly, the car was waved down by a tall young officer. The jolly grin on the weather-stained features could belong to only one man. "My son, Kingsley!" he cried.

Sir Arthur visited the French and Italian fronts and returned to work on his six-volume history, *The British Campaign in France and Flanders.* He watched the tide of battle turn slowly in favor of the Allies—then more decisively as fresh troops from America were thrown into the weary lines.

In September, 1918, the Australian government invited him to visit their front lines. From a grandstand position, only five hundred yards from the Hindenburg Line, Sir Arthur saw the fatal rift made by the Allied advance—the rift that was the beginning of the end for the Germans.

19. *Beyond Life*

"Where are our dead?" The question swelled in volume and urgency as longer casualty lists appeared in English papers. The men marched off to war, young, vital. The bands played. The soldiers waved, laughing. Then silence.

"He was there," cried the mothers, the sweethearts, the sisters. "Then a shell exploded, and there was nothing. A battered helmet, a dog tag, perhaps a muddy boot or a tarnished button. But where is he?" they wailed.

In 1915, the *International Psychic Gazette* addressed the question to a number of prominent men and women: "What would you say in consolation to those in grief?"

Conan Doyle's reply was brief. "I can say nothing worth saying. Time only is the healer."

In his own heart and mind the answer was not so clear. He had spent a lifetime trying to penetrate the veil he felt hid Truth. Even spiritualism seemed to offer only glimmerings of what lay beyond that veil.

"Yet it does seem to answer the immediate question," Sir Arthur admitted, "does death end all?"

The world and, worst of all, his own dear family were suffering grief that he was helpless to assuage. Lottie had lost her husband and Connie her only son. Jean's best friend,

Lily Loder-Symonds, who lived with them at Windlesham, had three brothers killed in the Ypres salient.

But Lily did not need his help. She claimed that she received messages from her brothers and her friend Malcolm Leckie. She had developed the power of automatic writing, so was able to record their communications. Arthur watched her for weeks, trying to discover just what did happen during her "conversations."

"Some power seemed to take possession of her arm and write things which are purported to come from the dead," he admitted, but regarded the whole procedure with suspicion. "It is easy to deceive oneself," he said to Jean. "How can you tell that she is not unconsciously dramatizing strands of her own personality?"

"But Arthur," Jean pointed out, "the communications are full of military detail that Lily couldn't possibly know. And one of her brothers named a Belgian he had met. We discovered this was so."

This from Jean who had always been frightened by the idea that souls might communicate from beyond the grave.

"It is impressive!" Arthur conceded. For some time he had been convinced that psychic phenomena such as table tapping and moving lights were of little significance of themselves. But could they be a signal, like the ringing of a phone, that someone was there with a message? The mind of Sherlock Holmes demanded proof. Then Arthur received a direct message from Malcolm Leckie—a message so personal he would never discuss it.

"The subject could have been known to no one except Malcolm and me," he declared. He considered the experience to be the proof he sought.

I seemed suddenly to see that this subject with which I had so long dallied was not merely a study of force outside the rules of science, but that it was something tremendous, a breaking down of the walls between two worlds, a direct undeniable message from beyond, a call of hope and of guidance to the human race at the time of its deepest affliction. . . .

Within a year after writing those words in *The New Revelation* that "call of hope" became a personal necessity.

London was dark with autumn rains as it waited out the final days of war. Kingsley, invalided home because of wounds, died of influenza on October 28.

"My only son by my first marriage," Sir Arthur wrote in his diary. "One of the grandest boys in body and soul that ever a father was blessed with."

The next blow came in February, 1919, when Innes Doyle, who had returned from France a brigadier-general with the Legion of Honor for distinguished service, died of pneumonia.

"My son and my brother!"

Arthur Conan Doyle had to believe that the doors were not closed, but only ajar.

Having made up his mind, spiritualism became a religion to Sir Arthur.

In the days of universal sorrow and loss . . . it was borne in upon me that the knowledge which had come to me thus was not for my own consolation alone, but that God had placed me in a very special position for conveying it to that world which needed it so badly . . . my gradual religious development, my books, which gave me an introduction to the public, my modest fortune, which enables me to convey the message, and my physical strength which, at 60, is still sufficient to stand arduous tours and to fill the largest halls for an hour and a half with my voice.

The great voice, the facile pen, carried its urgent message to the far corners of the earth, to Australia, New Zealand, America and Africa.

Sir Arthur explained his belief in spiritualism with the same simple logic he used to explain a Sherlock Holmes mystery. The soul survives death, he claimed, not as a disembodied spirit, but in an "etheric" body, which resembled the individual at the best period of his earthly life. In this form, the soul could return, with the aid of a medium, whose own personality left his body to make room for the visitor. While possessed of a spirit, the medium spoke in the voice of the possessor.

"I have listened to prophecies, quickly fulfilled," declared Conan Doyle. "My own wife has filled notebooks with information utterly beyond her understanding while her body was used by another spirit. Unlettered men acting as mediums have written passages in which I recognise the style and handwriting of a dead author. I have heard singing beyond earthly power.

"A closed mind," warned Sir Arthur, "means an earthbound soul."

The Ma'am opposed her son's belief in spiritualism until the day she died in 1920. But Sir Arthur did not fight his last battle alone. Jean and the children shared his journeys and his beliefs. His eldest son Denis, like Jean, received messages. In *Phineas Speaks* are recorded long conversations between Denis and his departed stepbrother Kingsley.

Though his beliefs turned many against him, audiences still flocked to see their beloved Sherlock Holmes.

"But as much to scoff, or out of curiosity, to see what ails me, as any other reason," Sir Arthur admitted ruefully.

He never lost his lusty sense of humor. When listeners heckled him, he fought back vigorously. One evening he

knocked over the water pitcher on the reporters beside the
platform.

"Well," laughed Conan Doyle. "I may not have converted
you, but at any rate, I have baptised you."

Harry Houdini, the famed American magician, was an
avid student of the occult. He met Conan Doyle during a
visit to England in 1920, and the two men had many stimu-
lating arguments. Sir Arthur found the Great Houdini's
knowledge of spiritualism as wide as his own, but their atti-
tudes were opposed. Houdini was as skeptical as Sir Arthur
was convinced of its value and importance to the world.

"I know all the tricks of the trade," Houdini reminded
Sir Arthur. "Psychic phenomena such as spirit writing and
appearances could be easily engineered by a clever medium.
I fooled Teddy Roosevelt himself with a slate writing trick."

"I am eager as you to expose fraudulent mediums," Conan
Doyle agreed, "and am always on the lookout for tricks. But
I have witnessed many true revelations."

In America, two years later, Houdini invited Sir Arthur to
a Magicians' Club dinner. Some scenes from the movie of
Doyle's *Lost World* were shown, then Houdini peformed his
famous locked-trunk trick. Handcuffed, tied in a bag, then
enclosed in an ironbound trunk, he was out within minutes.

"You could only perform such tricks by "dematerializing,"
insisted Conan Doyle. Indian fakirs claimed the ability to
"dematerialize" or dissolve their physical bodies, then rema-
terialize later.

No matter how Houdini argued that his feats were accomplished by purely physical means, Sir Arthur was certain that
the magician was receptive to psychic mysteries.

Sir Arthur's moments of relaxation during those crusading
years were few. During brief rest periods at Windlesham, his
pen never rested.

Besides his many books on psychics and his accounts of

his travels as an evangelist in that cause, he produced a new Sherlock Holmes series, *The Case-Book of Sherlock Holmes.* Holmes consistently refused to believe in the supernatural.

Professor Challenger was another matter. In *The Land of Mist* the aging professor was troubled by the death of his beloved wife, yet skeptical of life beyond the grave. Edward Malone, the athletic Irish reporter, finally converted the hard-bitten old scientist. The fictional conversion was an ideal vehicle for Conan Doyle to outline his own beliefs.

"Thank God that book is done!" he wrote his editor, Greenhough Smith. "It was so important to me that I feared I might pass away before it was done."

Doctors had long warned Sir Arthur that his aging heart would not stand the demands he put upon it.

"It is not a question of age," he told them, "but of what must be done. I am sustained by other forces."

And so he appeared to be, for he labored five more years. In 1927, Oscar Slater was released after twenty years of living death in Peterhead prison. Like Edalji, he was still considered legally guilty and so received no compensation. Conan Doyle had proof of his innocence as well as testimony indicating the identity of the true culprit.

His findings had planted a seed of doubt in the mind of Detective-Lieutenant John Thomson Trench of the Glasgow police. By persistent questioning, Trench had uncovered new evidence. The finger of guilt pointed to a relative of Marion Gilchrist's, as Conan Doyle had surmised. But there was too little proof. Lieutenant Trench was discharged for his diligence, and the matter was forgotten.

Despite his age and weakening heart, Sir Arthur supplied Slater with money and personal support in his court battle to establish his innocence. When the case was won, Conan Doyle set out to tour South Africa, Rhodesia and Kenya, where he spoke for the first time over a radio network that carried his clear deep voice for hundreds of miles. He predicted the eventual union of the English-speaking people.

"Some great watershed of human experience may be passed within a few years," he told audiences, "the greatest our long-suffering race has yet encountered."

In London, he opened a psychical bookshop with Mary in charge. At seventy, he visited Scandinavia, and planned to carry his message to Rome, Athens, Constantinople. But as he hurried back to London for Armistice Day services, his great heart collapsed.

They carried him from the boat-train to his flat at 15 Buckingham Palace Mansions. The doctors gave him oxygen and warned him to cancel all speaking engagements. But on Sunday, November 11, 1929, he spoke at Albert Hall. That evening he spoke again at Queen's Hall. Afterward, with snowflakes drifting around his bare head, he greeted those who had been unable to find seats inside.

He seemed to laugh at bodily ills. Though he moved slowly, he continued to improve into the spring of 1930. But even his great will could not defeat the clock. Though neither he nor Jean nor any of their children would admit to such a thing as death, his heart did stop beating on July 7, and his spirit went to dwell elsewhere.

Ten thousand people attended a memorial service in London's Albert Hall. Sir Arthur Conan Doyle was buried in the rose garden at Windlesham, near the garden hut where he often wrote.

"He was a king amongst men," wrote one friend, "and a tremendous personality for good. I shall never see his like again."

On his simple headstone of British oak was described his name, the date of his birth, and four simple words:

STEEL TRUE, BLADE STRAIGHT

There was no date of death. The halls of Windlesham would never again echo to his heavy tread and hearty voice. In Baker Street, modern buildings block out memories of Sherlock Holmes' lodgings. But for those who love him, Sir Arthur Conan Doyle will never die.

On a July morning in 1955, Sir Arthur and Lady Jean were moved from their resting place in the garden of Windlesham to the little churchyard of All Saints, Minstead, in the New Forest. Only their youngest daughter Jean, a Group Commander in the Women's Air Force (WAF), attended the simple ceremony.

Thus, one quarter of a century to the day after his passing, Sir Arthur returned to Saxon England where lived and fought the hardy men whose code and courage had ever been his ideal—Sir Nigel Loring and his *White Company*.

Bibliography

Books about Arthur Conan Doyle and His Times

Baldwin, Hanson W. *Seafights and Shipwrecks.* Hanover House, Garden City, N. Y., 1955.

Barrie, James. *The Greenwood Hat.* Charles Scribner's Sons, New York, 1938.

Blakeney, Thomas S. *Sherlock Holmes, Fact or Fiction?* John Murray, London, 1932.

Carr, John Dickson. *The Life of Sir Arthur Conan Doyle.* John Murray, London, 1954.

Doyle, Adrian Conan (with John Dickson Carr). *The Exploits of Sherlock Holmes.* Random House, New York, 1954.

———. *The True Conan Doyle.* Coward-McCann, Inc., New York, 1946.

Ernst, Bernard M. L. and Carrington, Hereward. *Houdini and Conan Doyle, The Story of a Strange Friendship.* A. & C. Boni, Inc., New York, 1932.

Hardwick, John Michael Drinkow and Hardwick, Mollie. *The Man Who Was Sherlock Holmes.* Doubleday and Co., Garden City, 1964.

Hoehling, A. A. *The Great War At Sea.* Thomas Y. Crowell Company, New York, 1965.

Hoehling, A. A. and Mary. *The Last Voyage of the Lusitania.* Henry Holt & Co., 1956.

Klinefelter, Walter. *Sherlock Holmes in Portrait and Profile.* Syracuse University Press, Syracuse, 1963.

Morley, Christopher. *Sherlock Holmes and Dr. Watson, A Textbook on Friendship.* Harcourt, Brace & Co., New York, 1944.

Pearson, Hesketh. *Conan Doyle, His Life and Art.* Methuen & Co., Ltd., London, 1943.

Sir Arthur Conan Doyle, 1859-1959 (Centenary Volume), John Murray, London, 1959.

Williams, Beryl and Epstein, Samuel. *The Great Houdini.* Julian Messner, Inc., New York, 1950.

Books by Arthur Conan Doyle

The works of Arthur Conan Doyle have appeared in countless editions and in forty-two different languages. In making a list of suggested reading, I have chosen only the most recent reprints.

The Adventures of Sherlock Holmes. Junior Deluxe Edition, Garden City, N. Y., 1956.

The Black Doctor, and Other Tales of Terror and Mystery. George H. Doran, New York, 1925.

The Boys' Sherlock Holmes (arranged by Howard Haycraft). Harper & Bros., New York, 1961.

British Campaign in France and Flanders. George H. Doran, New York, 1918-19.

The Captain of the Polestar and Other Tales. Longmans, Green & Co., New York, 1913.

Captain Sharkey and Other Tales of Pirates. George H. Doran, New York, 1925.

The Case for Spirit Photography. George H. Doran, New York, 1923.

The Case of Oscar Slater. George H. Doran, New York, 1912.

The Coming of the Fairies. George H. Doran, New York, 1922.

The Complete Sherlock Holmes. Doubleday & Co., Garden City, 1953.

The Crime of the Congo. Doubleday, Page & Co., New York, 1909.

The Croxley Master and Other Tales of Ring and Camp. George H. Doran, New York, 1952.

Danger and Other Stories. George H. Doran, New York, 1919.

The Glorious Hussar, The Best of the Exploits and Adventures of Brigadier Gerard. Walker & Co., New York, 1961.

The Great Boer War. McClure, Phillips & Co., New York, 1902.

Great Britain and the Next War. Small, Maynard & Co., New York, 1914.

The Guards Came Through and Other Poems. George H. Doran, New York, 1920.

The Lost World. Looking Glass Library, Random House, New York, 1959.

Memories and Adventures. Little, Brown & Co., Boston, 1924.

Micah Clarke. D. Appleton & Co., New York, 1902.

Our African Winter. John Murray, London, 1929.

Our American Adventure. George H. Doran, New York, 1923.

Our Second American Adventure. Little, Brown & Co., Boston, 1924.

Professor Challenger Stories. John Murray, London, 1952.

The Refugees, A Tale of Two Continents. Harper & Bros., New York, 1921.

The Stark Munro Letters. D. Appleton & Co., New York, 1894.

The White Company. Dodd, Mead & Co., New York, 1962.

Index

184

About the Author

Mary Hoehling was born in Worcester, Massachusetts, attended school there and in Noroton, Connecticut. After two years at Wheaton College, she left to marry and settle in Washington, D. C. Her first published "work" was a poem about a windswept beach which she wrote at the age of twelve and was published in the school paper. As she went through school, historic events and personalities captured her imagination, and when her children began complaining of the dullness of history in textbooks, she decided to try her hand at writing biography. She is married to the well-known author, A. A. Hoehling, and is herself the author of several biographies for young people.